RSC

D0351388

99 579

first
assessment

1 — Setting the Scene

With rising costs and growing demand, trusts must make more efficient use of district nursing services.

2 — Managing Demand for District Nursing Services

Some services are struggling because objectives are poorly defined, the referral process is imperfect and caseloads are not reviewed systematically.

3 — Improving the Quality of Care

To improve quality, trusts need effective systems for monitoring practice and implementing evidence-based care.

4 — Improving Service Efficiency

Trusts vary greatly in the ways that they deploy district nursing resources, without clear evidence about the effects on patients.

5 — Moving Forward

District nursing services need to evolve to match changes in patient needs and expectations and to meet the challenges posed by developments in the wider health and social care environment.

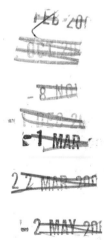

Contents

© Audit Commission 1999

First published in March 1999 by the Audit Commission for Local Authorities and the National Health Service in England and Wales, 1 Vincent Square, London SW1P 2PN

Typeset by Eighteen04 Design, Woodbridge, Suffolk.

Printed in the UK for the Audit Commission by Belmont Press.

ISBN 1 86240 149 7

Photographs: Janis Austin/Photofusion (p22), Garth Blore (p39) with thanks to Cornwall Healthcare Trust, Jacky Chapman/Format (p96), Simon Denton (cover, pp20, 41, 64, 72, 80, 86, 94) with thanks to Community Healthcare Bolton NHS Trust, reproduced with the kind permission of the Queens Nursing Institute (p3), Hilary Shedel (p106), Sam Tanner/Photofusion (pp11, 67), Mike Uttley (pp5, 14, 32, 54, 70, 77, 111) with thanks to North Kent NHS Trust (now part of the Thames Gateway NHS Trust) and Exeter & District Community Health Service NHS Trust.

Preface

1. Most of the professional nursing care provided in patients' homes is delivered by district nursing staff. Each year about 2.75 million people are patients of the service and more than 36 million patient contacts take place. Many of these patients are elderly and frail. Each year, half of the population aged 85 and over is seen by a district nurse; many are seen two or three times a week. And yet the apparent invisibility of much district nursing practice means that it is often understood in only the broadest, and most simplistic, of terms. Its public stereotyping as an unhurried, low-tech, backwater service – a service that time forgot – is both inaccurate and undeserved.

2. Much of the income of community trusts derives directly from district nursing services and district nursing staff often form the single largest group of community trust employees. Nationally, expenditure on district nursing services was approximately £650 million in 1997/98. Trust managers, anxious to maintain service contracts, express uncertainty about whether district nurses are being deployed as flexibly as they might, whether some of the services that they provide – for example, at night – are as efficient as they ought to be, and how district nursing staff – operating out of many different premises across sometimes considerable geographical areas – can best be managed. District nurses themselves raise questions about the ways in which they are managed and the appropriateness of some of the patients who are referred to them. They also question the demands placed on them to deliver care to patients who are being discharged from hospital earlier and with greater nursing needs.

3. The importance of the service to patients and their informal carers, the widely varying levels of resource input and use, the opportunities to improve the quality of care delivered and the key role that all community nurses are expected to play in primary care groups (local health groups in Wales), make this review both timely and pertinent. The Audit Commission chose the study because district nursing is a comparatively under researched service; the chief executives of NHS community trusts strongly supported the proposal during consultation.

4. Over the next year, the Audit Commission's appointed auditors will be assessing where each trust in England and Wales stands in relation to these issues and how services for patients can be improved.

5.   The study was carried out by Dr Ian Seccombe, Rob Burns and
Gabrielle Smith (RN) from the Audit Commission's Health Studies
Directorate, under the direction of Dr Jocelyn Cornwell and Dr Jonathan
Boyce. Jenny Bartholomew (RN), Dr Nicky Britten, Alan Chu, Wendy
Coffey (RN), Monica Haynes, Samantha Jackson, Jo Marsh, Professor
Fiona Ross (RN), Adrienne Shaw (RN) and Eileen Shepherd (RN)
contributed as members of the study team or as consultants to it. The
study team benefited enormously from the co-operation of staff in the
NHS trusts and GP practices that were visited, and is grateful to all the
nurses, patients and carers who gave their time to complete
questionnaires or to be interviewed. An advisory group of practitioners
and other interested parties provided further assistance and insight
(Appendix 1). As always, responsibility for the contents and conclusions
rests solely with the Audit Commission.

1

Setting the Scene

District nurses provide most of the professional nursing care given to patients who live at home. But trusts face a rising demand for these services at a time when large numbers of district nurses are nearing retirement and fewer are qualifying. Given these pressures, trusts need to review the ways in which they organise, manage and deliver district nursing services.

What is district nursing?

6.   Relatives, friends, neighbours and volunteers play a vital role in looking after dependent people living at home; indeed, they provide most of the care and support that people need. Since the pioneering days of 1860s Liverpool, when the Victorian philanthropist William Rathbone employed Mary Robinson (arguably the first district nurse) to work with the 'sick poor' (Ref. 1), district nurses have complemented that care and support [CASE HISTORY A] as the main providers of professional nursing care in people's homes.[1]*

The patients

7.   Care for chronic illness, terminal illness, incontinence, wound management and diabetes are the main reasons why district nurses see patients. Many (more than 60 per cent) of these patients have multiple nursing needs. The majority (62 per cent) of district nursing patients are aged 65 and over; one in four people aged 75 to 84 are district nursing patients. But district nurses also see younger people; 4 per cent of their patients are aged under 16.[2]

---

*   There is a glossary of technical terms at the end of the report. Footnotes are also gathered together at the end.

CASE HISTORY A

This 80-year-old man has had several strokes. His adult daughter moved in to care for him when he was discharged from hospital. She has two school-aged children. He cannot be left on his own in the house. Care assistants help him to wash and dress and sit with him for a couple of hours each week to give her some rest.

The district nurses visit twice a week to wash out his catheter bag and take blood. They have organised a ramp and a rail and are also trying to obtain a buzzer so that he can call for help at night. He wears continence pads day and night, but has been told that he can have only one kind, so he cannot have pads to protect the bed. He has a plastic sheet for the bed and his daughter places three ordinary pads on top. His daughter values the nursing care and the fact that she has someone to talk to. 'They talk to Dad as well, they don't come in and do everything and ignore him and not talk to him. They come in and talk, basically just talk and have a laugh.' They give her advice about his diet and fluids and make sure that he takes his tablets. 'Basically I needed someone to talk to and the nurse was there. She wasn't there just for my Dad, she was there for me as well, and I like that.'

Source: Audit Commission patients' and carers' study (for methodology see para.42 and Box C.)

Some patients will have only one visit but, for many, district nursing staff are frequent and continuing visitors.

8. Some patients will have only one visit but, for many, district nursing staff are frequent and continuing visitors. Almost half of the 2,168 patients on the 21 caseloads reviewed by the Audit Commission were visited every week, including some (5 per cent) who were seen at least once a day. One in six had been a district nursing patient for more than three years.

9. About 2.75 million people receive care from district nursing services each year.[3] And the number of patients has increased (by nearly 8 per cent) since 1991/92 [EXHIBIT 1]. The number of new referrals (reported in official statistics as 'initial contacts') also grew over the 1990s, although the most recent figures show a decline.

10. But, in England, both the number of patients and the number of new referrals are lower now than in the late 1980s. And the total number of patient contacts (35.9 million in 1997/98) has fallen by 8.5 per cent since 1988/89 and by 6 per cent since 1994/95. The average number of contacts per episode (13.6) is also lower. The reasons for these trends are not known with certainty, but in part they are explained by the movement of patients with personal care needs from district nursing to social services following implementation of the NHS and Community Care Act in 1993.

11. The number of district nursing contacts in residential homes has increased by 13 per cent since 1991/92. But the number of places in residential homes has remained fairly steady throughout the 1990s, following rapid growth during the 1980s. Although residential homes consistently account for about 7 per cent of all district nursing contacts, the proportion of the residential home population being seen by district nurses is rising as the average age of the residents rises.

EXHIBIT 1

District nursing: first and initial contacts, 1988/89 to 1997/98, England

Numbers of patients have increased in recent years, although the numbers have decreased since the late 1980s.

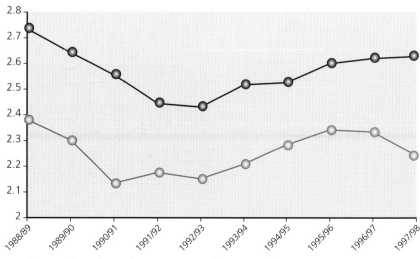

Contacts (millions)

○— **Number of people receiving care (first contacts)**
○— **Number of new episodes of care in the year (initial contacts)**

Source: Department of Health statistics

...trends point to increasing demands on the service...

12. There is little systematic evidence about the dependency of patients whom district nurses see in residential homes but there is evidence that overall dependency levels in residential care have risen substantially (Ref. 2). And nurses report that, for cost-saving purposes, some patients who need 24-hour nursing care are being placed in residential homes (where they will be seen by district nurses) rather than in nursing homes (where care is provided by nursing staff).

13. Surveys conducted by individual trusts have identified significant year-on-year increases in the number and proportion of very elderly patients and an increasing emphasis on 'technical' (as opposed to personal) nursing care (Refs. 3 and 4). Trusts have also reported faster patient turnover on caseloads, increases in the numbers of acute and post-surgical patients and greater reliance on qualified district nurses rather than nursing auxiliaries or healthcare assistants carrying out delegated tasks (Ref. 5). These trends point to increasing demands on the service and in particular on the qualified staff.

14. The very elderly (those aged 85 and over) represent a growing proportion of the district nursing caseload. In England, they account for one in six of all patients compared with one in eight only five years ago. During 1997/98, almost half of the very elderly were seen by district nurses. They represent more than one-quarter of those on the caseloads reviewed in this study and can have a disproportionate impact on workloads. One in five sees a district nurse more than once a week, most have multiple care packages, one-fifth have been district nursing patients for three years or more and the majority also receive care from social services.

The nurses

15. District nurses are registered nurses with an additional qualification that enables them to assess (and reassess) patients' and carers' needs in their homes, to plan appropriate services for patients, to implement and evaluate programmes of planned nursing care, to manage a nursing team and to supervise the performance of all staff attached to the team. Crucially, district nurses work at the boundary of health and social care delivery and make a major contribution to the multidisciplinary assessment of patients, the formulation of care packages and liaison with social services and others in service delivery [CASE HISTORY B].

16. District nursing staff work in teams. As well as at least one qualified district nurse, most teams also include one or more registered (but not district nursing qualified) nurses as well as nursing auxiliaries or healthcare assistants [BOX A].

CASE HISTORY B

This patient, in his eighties, has had a double amputation followed by a severe stroke which has paralysed his left side. His daughter looks after him. He is *'having trouble with his bowels. Before he'd tell me if he wanted to go to the toilet, but now, forget it, he just doesn't know.'* Two carers from Age Concern come in every morning to give him a bed bath. The district nurse taught them how to lift him and turn him. They used to come in the evening but the daughter stopped this because she did not know when they were coming and she found it easier to do it herself.

The district nurse has paid a visit in the past month to sort out the paperwork but has delegated his care to auxiliaries. They visit three times a week to give him an enema. The only thing the daughter feels she needs is more respite care. The district nurse has put her in touch with a carers' organisation which provides her with one afternoon off a week. She likes to see the same carers and auxiliaries as the relationships are important to her. *'It's a half hour where, if I've got any worries, I can say to the girls and I know it goes straight back.'*

Source: Audit Commission patients' and carers' study

BOX A

District nursing teams: grades and roles

District nursing sister – G and H

Registered nurses with an additional district nursing qualification. Continuing responsibility for the assessment of care needs, the development and implementation and evaluation of programmes of care and the setting of standards of care. District nurses with additional responsibilities in teaching (that is, community practice teachers) and management, or who are clinical nurse specialists, are likely to be in posts at grade H.

Community staff nurse – D, E , F

Registered nurses providing nearly all forms of nursing care without direct supervision.

Nursing auxiliary – B

Unregistered nursing auxiliaries or healthcare assistants carrying out assigned tasks – depending on local agreements and training.

The numbers of staff with district nursing qualifications has been reducing.

17. The numbers of staff employed by district nursing services have changed little over the last ten years but the number with district nursing qualifications has been reducing. There are about 13,460 (10,839 whole time equivalent – wte) qualified district nurses in NHS employment, one-quarter of whom work part-time. Working with them are 18,200 other registered nurses and approximately 6,950 nursing auxiliaries [see **APPENDIX 2**]. But the resources that health authorities invest in district nursing vary widely when compared with the populations they serve.

18. In the past, most district nursing services were organised on a district-wide basis. During the 1980s the concept of the primary healthcare team – in which district nurses and health visitors are attached to a GP practice – gained widespread favour.

19. But the 1986 Cumberlege report (Ref. 6) concluded that attachment could lead to gaps and confusion in the delivery of primary care and the possibility that some needs would go unrecognised, voluntary and local authority services would not be properly integrated with primary care and resources would be wasted by unnecessary travel.[4]

20. Nevertheless, in all but a handful of trusts most (more than 80 per cent) district nursing staff are now 'attached' to one or more GP practice(s).[5] That is, they provide care for the patients registered with the practice(s), but they are not necessarily based in the GP's premises. These patients may be geographically dispersed and the idea of a district nurse being a well-known figure in the local community is largely an image from the past. In inner-city areas, a qualified district nurse may work for several small practices, while staff nurses and auxiliaries may work between teams.

21. Most district nurses see the benefit of attachment in the form of closer working relations with GPs and practice nurses and the opportunity to run practice-based clinics. But there is not much evidence to substantiate the idea of effective teamworking in primary healthcare. Practice attachment can, as Cumberlege anticipated, lead to inequity and poor response to changes in demand. In many trusts, district nurses are allocated to practices on a historic basis. For example, resources may initially have been allocated on the basis of referrals. This may disadvantage patients of low referring practices. And, there may be no mechanism to revise these allocations when populations change. Where trusts have compared resources to potential demand, they have often found an apparently inequitable distribution [**EXHIBIT 2**].[6]

EXHIBIT 2

WTE district nurses per 10,000 practice list population in one trust

The allocation of district nurses to practices may be inequitable when compared with crude proxies for demand.

Source: Audit Commission study site

WTE district nursing staff per 10,000 practice list population

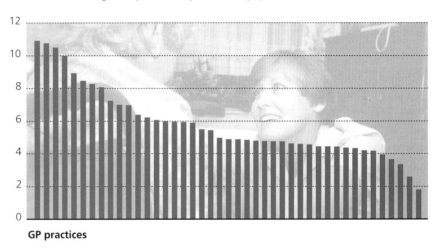

GP practices

22. Rigid practice allocation (which was reinforced by GP fundholding) may also cause inefficiency by, for example, preventing nurses attached to neighbouring practices from covering for each other, leading to higher travel costs and greater use of temporary staff.

23. In addition, attachment can create tensions between nurses and trust managers. Nurses can feel conflicts of loyalty and confusion about whom they work for and to whom they are accountable. Trust managers sometimes find it difficult to strike a balance between meeting the wishes of GPs, particularly where they have been fundholders, and providing an equitable and efficient service to the population in the trust's catchment area.

Practice nurses

24. In contrast with the district nursing workforce, the numbers of practice nurses employed in England have grown markedly through the 1990s in response to the needs of general practice and the provision of general medical services (Ref. 7).[7] Much of the work specified in the new (1990) general medical practitioner contract – health promotion, immunisation targets, cervical screening, annual assessments for over 75s – could be delegated to nurses who could increase the income potential of general practices.

...the roles of district nurses and practice nurses can overlap...

25. Even where district nursing resources are allocated evenly, resource differences may still appear because of the employment of practice nurses [EXHIBIT 3].[8] Lower rates of practice nurse provision are associated with areas of greater healthcare needs. Recent national research has concluded that *'practice nurse numbers scarcely corresponded with healthcare needs'* (Ref. 8).

26. Broadly speaking, practice nurses see patients who are able to attend the GP surgery or health centre. But there is no consensus on the scope of practice nursing or the degree of specialisation. And the roles of district nurses and practice nurses can overlap; for example, in chronic disease management. It is important, therefore, that both groups provide consistent advice and care.

An ageing workforce

27. Although district nursing has a lower rate of turnover and vacancies[9] than any other area of nursing (Ref. 9), it is likely to notice the effects of an ageing workforce earlier. The average age of qualified district nurses is 45.4 (compared with 39 for all registered nurses) and 27 per cent are aged 50 or over[10] [EXHIBIT 4]. In part this older average age reflects the fact that district nursing is a post-registration qualification often taken up by nurses who have first had experience of working in a hospital setting or as community staff nurses. But it also reflects reductions in the numbers qualifying as district nurses in recent years. These have been falling as entries to training have declined.[11] Study site trusts, not only those in inner cities, report a lack of job applicants and increasing problems in filling vacancies.

28. District nurses who joined the NHS Pension Scheme before March 1995 can retire with full benefits at age 55 or take voluntary early retirement, with reduced benefits, from age 50. Almost half the district nurses aged 50 and over who responded to the Audit Commission's survey said that they intended to retire before they were 60, including 29 per cent who wanted to retire at 55. The extended age range at which district nurses can retire makes it difficult for trusts to forecast retirements with accuracy. In practice their forecasts tend to be over-optimistic. For example, one trust assumed that there would be no retirements over the next five years, even though one-third of district nurses were aged over 50 and 6 per cent were already over 55. In another trust, the forecast was for one retirement per year, despite having 40 district nurses aged over 50 at the time of the forecast.

EXHIBIT 3

WTE district and practice nurses per 10,000 practice list population

Resource differences may appear because of the employment of practice nurses.

WTE district nursing staff and practice nurses per 10,000 practice list population

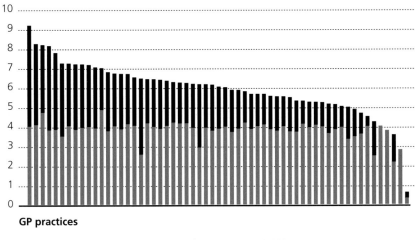

GP practices

■ District nurses per 10,000   ■ Practice nurses per 10,000

Source: Audit Commission study site

EXHIBIT 4

Age profile of qualified district nurses

More than one-quarter of district nurses are aged 50 or over.

Percentage of qualified district nurses

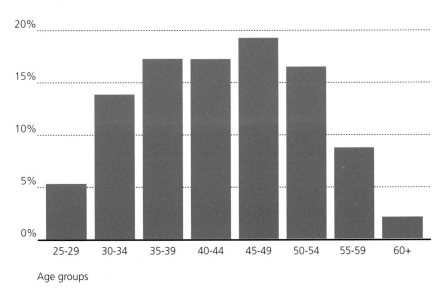

Age groups

Source: NHS Executive and Welsh Office statistics

29. A key question for NHS trusts (and for their education and training consortia) is, will the numbers qualifying as district nurses be sufficient to replace those who retire (or leave for other reasons) and to meet any additional growth in demand? Current forecasts suggest an increase in the number of qualified staff in post of just over 2 per cent between 1997/98 and 2001/02. But demand for newly qualified district nurses is projected to fall from 1998/99.[12] If the demand for newly qualified district nurses is underestimated by employers, or local education and training consortia, then there is a serious risk of under-commissioning training places. Moreover, the Audit Commission's survey of trusts shows that the number of community practice teachers in district nursing has fallen by 8 per cent in three years. Clearly, a shortage of teachers could constrain efforts to increase the number of qualified district nurses.

The trusts

30. There is considerable diversity in the organisation and delivery of district nursing between trusts, making the task of evaluating services particularly difficult. For example:

- the populations that district nurses serve may be highly concentrated in inner cities or spread over considerable rural areas;

- trusts vary in their potential to benefit from economies of scale. Some employ up to 300 wte nursing staff, while others have fewer than 50 wte staff;

- some district nurses see patients more frequently than others. There is a threefold difference between trusts in the average number of contacts per patient per year [EXHIBIT 5];

- some district nurses see more than one-third of their patients in clinics, while others have little, or no, clinic-based provision; and

- while half of all trusts provide some district nursing services around the clock, others have no, or very limited, staff availability beyond 5pm.

EXHIBIT 5

Ratio of total contacts to first contacts

There is a threefold difference between trusts in the average number of contacts per patient per year.

Average number of contacts per patient

Trusts

Source: Department of Health statistics

31. The proportion of the population aged 75 and over that is receiving care from district nursing varies considerably from one trust to another. In some, more than half the over-75s receive district nursing care, in others it is fewer than one-third [**EXHIBIT 6**]. The variation that characterises district nursing would not be a problem if it reflected differences in need or in what local users want. But there is no convincing evidence to support either argument.

32. What the service covers in one trust may not be exactly what it covers in another. Services have evolved locally, partly in response to the availability of other services – for example, the provision of care by social services and voluntary groups; the availability of hospice places; and the employment of practice nurses.

33. District nursing services can be evaluated on their own; that is the purpose of this report. But how they fit with other services is very important. District nursing is an essential ingredient in the complex pattern of support that is needed to sustain people in their own homes. Perhaps the most crucial role of the service is its collaboration with other agencies and health professionals in developing, implementing and managing broad packages of care. Collaboration is important because GPs control access to secondary and community health services through patient referrals. And social services departments manage funding for home care services and for residential and nursing home places. Social services also control access through assessment and care management. The ability of district nursing to achieve its objectives for patients is therefore affected by the behaviour of GPs and social services staff.

EXHIBIT 6

First contacts with over-75s per 1,000 population over 75 by trust

In some trusts more than half of those over 75 receive district nursing care.

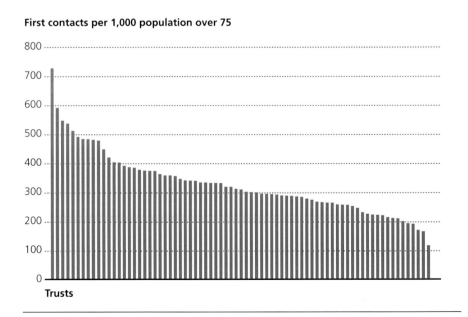

First contacts per 1,000 population over 75

Source: Audit Commission survey of trusts

The commissioners

Contact figures are inadequate for monitoring patient care or workloads, or for managing performance and contracting.

34. Health authorities generally purchase district nursing services via a block contract which relates to the number of patient contacts made.[13] A contact is any face-to-face meeting between district nursing staff and an individual patient or patient's proxy, where treatment or advice is given, and the location is anywhere other than a hospital ward or outpatient clinic.[14] Contracts with GP fundholders were based on the number of wte nursing staff required by individual practices.

35. In neither case were contracts based on casemix, the needs of the local population, the grade of staff involved or on the outcomes of care. Contact figures are therefore inadequate for monitoring patient care or workloads, or for managing performance and contracting purposes, because they ignore the purpose, appropriateness and length of visit.[15]

36. Frustrated by the inadequacy of contacts as a contract currency and as a basis for making decisions on resource allocation, some trusts have developed 'packages of care' for measuring district nursing [BOX B]. Packages of care include all of the nursing care that may be given to a patient with a particular condition.[16] Some patients will receive all elements of the package, while others will require only parts of it. Individual patients can receive more than one package at a time and can move between packages over time.

BOX B

An alternative basis for contracting

In 1994, one health authority started work with four trusts to develop a tool to identify what care was being provided by district nurses. As a result of this work, 11 care packages were developed and clinical protocols written for each. The trusts were then asked to consider how these packages of care could be used for future contracting purposes.

In June 1996, the District Nurse Practice Development Group at the lead trust (North Kent NHS Trust) was asked to create standards for these packages and a coding system for district nurses to record the packages of care that they were delivering. Significant effort at the trust (funded by the health authority) has been put into developing an audit tool to ensure the consistent use of codes by all staff. All four trusts have now trained their district nurses in the coding system and the health authority started collecting data from these trusts in April 1998. The aim is to contract for packages of care from April 1999.

The lead trust is now developing a set of core competencies that are required for the assessment and delivery of packages of care. It has agreed a framework for developing a skills audit tool to assist staff in assessing their knowledge, skills, ability and their understanding of clinical practice and competence related to the assessment and delivery of packages of care.

Source: Audit Commission study site

37. Rapid growth in the number of elderly people, and particularly the very elderly, has significant resource implications for district nursing [EXHIBIT 7]. The NHS White Paper (Ref. 10) suggests that, over the next decade, the NHS will have to provide services for an extra 100,000 people aged 85 and over. Other trends, especially the increasing wish for people to die at home, will also have an impact. The proportion of people dying at home has fallen from a peak of 60 per cent in the 1960s to around 22 per cent today. But research has shown that many more patients wish to die at home than do so (Ref. 11). One in twelve patients on the caseloads reviewed by the Audit Commission were receiving care for a terminal illness. Many of these patients were seen more than once a week and nearly 10 per cent were seen daily or more than once a day.

38. Demographic change also means that the growing elderly population will be supported by proportionately fewer people of working age. And social change means that fewer families are willing, or able, to provide as much of the care for dependent relatives as they have in the past. Taken together, these changes mean that the demands for nursing care delivered to patients at home are likely to grow significantly.

What the report aims to do

39. This study was undertaken at a time of immense policy change foreshadowed in the White Papers, *The new NHS – Modern and Dependable* (Ref. 10) and *NHS Wales – Putting Patients First* (Ref. 12) and the September 1998 consultation documents, *Partnership in Action* (Ref. 13) and, in Wales, *Partnership for Improvement* (Ref. 14). These changes will lead, in April 1999, to the establishment of 481 primary care groups (PCGs) in England and 22 local health groups (LHGs) in Wales. Their stated purpose is to enable GPs, community nurses and other health and social care professionals to improve the health of their community and the delivery of care to patients.

EXHIBIT 7

Forecast population change in England and Wales, 1994 to 2034

Rapid growth in the numbers of elderly and very elderly people has significant resource implications for district nursing.

Age group populations expressed as a proportion of their 1994 levels

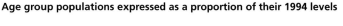
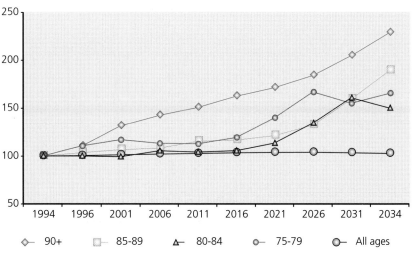

Source: Office of National Statistics' projections

The changes envisaged will have a profound impact on district nursing services...

40. This report aims to help trusts, and the new PCGs/LHGs, to recognise and understand the variations described above and to assess how existing services are performing against the expectations set out in the White Papers.

41. District nursing is a complex service; a report of this size can explore only some aspects. The development of nurse prescribing is important in district nursing but lies outside the scope of this study. Equally, this report does not consider the management of aids and appliances (these are the subject of a new Audit Commission study), nor does it examine supplies or information technology (which have been covered in recent Audit Commission reports) (Refs. 15 and 16).

Study methods

42. The report is based primarily on visits in 1997/98 to seven NHS trusts (these 'study sites' are listed in Appendix 3) drawn from across England and Wales. This fieldwork included group discussions and interviews with trust managers and district nursing staff, analysis of patient, personnel and financial information systems, caseload reviews of 21 district nursing teams, examination of more than 1,614 activity diaries kept by district nursing staff, analysis of data on more than 3,400 referrals collected in a two-week prospective survey and reviews of assessment documentation for 321 patients. Additionally, 91 per cent (171) of NHS trusts with a district nursing service provided data on staffing, activity, costs and services in response to the Audit Commission's national survey. Further insights into the service and its performance came from in-depth interviews with patients and carers [BOX C], and from a postal questionnaire survey of 1,500 nurses which achieved a 76 per cent response. Appendix 4 provides details of these and the other data sources that were used.

The report structure

43. The White Papers set out an agenda for ensuring that the NHS makes best use of its resources to deliver better, more responsive and informed services. The changes that are envisaged will have a profound impact on the ways in which district nursing services are organised, managed and delivered. Important questions will be raised about the most effective ways of identifying need for district nursing services, of ensuring fair access to – and consistent quality of – those services, of integrating services so that patients' needs are central and their views are taken into account. This study addresses these questions.

- The new performance assessment framework means that trusts need to know that their district nursing services are being delivered on the basis of need and that resources are deployed as efficiently as possible. Chapter 2 considers how demand for district nursing can be managed to ensure fairer access to services and more efficient use of resources.

- Chapter 3 is about the quality of care provided by district nursing services. Two major areas of care provision where there is national clinical guidance – leg ulcers and continence – are used to explore two key aspects of quality: first, the quality of nursing assessment; and second, getting evidence about effectiveness into practice. The chapter also considers service quality from the perspective of patients and carers.

- Expenditure on district nursing services varies markedly between trusts. Chapter 4 examines the factors that contribute to this variation including numbers of staff employed, the mix of grades, the use of temporary staff, staff deployment and the provision of out-of-hours and clinic services.

- The report moves from examining services' current performance to look – in Chapter 5 – at the future and, in particular, at what district nursing services need to do in order to meet changing needs and to address the agenda for change set out in *The new NHS – Modern and Dependable* (Ref. 10).

BOX C

The patients' and carers' study

As part of this review, the Audit Commission asked the Department of General Practice and Primary Care at Guy's, King's and St Thomas' School of Medicine to undertake a study that would explore the views and experiences of a group of patients and carers which had recently used the district nursing service. A sample of 40 patients who had been visited by district nurses in March 1998 were selected from practices in the catchment areas of two NHS trusts. One trust covered parts of inner London and the other included a mixed urban and rural area in south-east England. Half of the patient sample had leg ulcers and half had continence problems – conditions that are used as probes throughout this study (see Chapter 3). Ten carers of patients with leg ulcers or continence problems were also selected. Ethical approval for the study was obtained and exclusion criteria were used to avoid approaching individuals who were unsuitable for interview on ethical grounds. The semi-structured interviews were conducted by an experienced nurse interviewer.

2

Managing Demand for District Nursing Services

Defining need for district nursing care is not straightforward, but the lack of clear service objectives and referral criteria leads to uncertainty and inefficiency. Patients who could benefit are not being referred, while others are referred inappropriately. And the lack of systematic caseload profiling can mean that patients remain 'on the books' for longer than they need to be. The recommendations call for trusts to define service objectives more clearly, to improve referral processes and to institute regular caseload review.

Introduction

44. The purpose of the district nursing service is not well defined. If there is consensus, it is about organising and delivering care to support people so that they can live in their own homes for as long as possible. But neither trusts nor health authorities have profiled their populations at a level that is sophisticated enough to predict the need for district nursing. If resources are to be managed efficiently and targeted at patients who will benefit, the objectives of the service need to be clearly stated. Currently, the service is demand-led and is defined mainly by the referrals that it attracts. But the referral process is imperfect.

45. District nursing has an open referral system. That is, anyone can be referred to it and patients are seldom turned away. But the absence of clear service objectives leads to uncertainty and inefficiency. Patients who could benefit from district nursing care may not be referred to the service, while others are referred inappropriately. Particular problems arise when patients leave hospital. Many community trusts employ liaison nurses, who are based in local acute hospitals, to promote more effective patient transfer, but problematic discharges continue. Referral is likely to remain the main means of identifying need for district nursing, so it is important that the process works well.

46. The conventional wisdom in district nursing is that caseloads are under increasing pressure as a result of factors such as the shift to community care, earlier hospital discharge and an increasingly elderly population. This pressure may also be, in part, a result of the open referral system and the absence of referral criteria. The lack of systematic caseload profiling can mean that patients who no longer have nursing needs nevertheless remain on the caseload. District nurses review the cases of individual patients on a regular basis at case conferences, when planning visits and at each patient encounter. But their approach focuses more on organising the team to meet the needs of patients currently on the caseload and less on systematically monitoring the casemix as a whole. And trust managers also tend to spend little time reviewing caseloads with their staff. This can lead to a mismatch between demand and resources.

Identifying need for district nursing

47. To judge the value for money of the district nursing service we would, ideally, be able to assess the extent to which it meets 'needs' (where 'need' is defined as 'potential to benefit from the service'). But defining what constitutes need for district nursing care is not straightforward. Few trusts have clearly identified what the service is for. By default, it is largely defined by the nurses themselves and by those who refer to them.

...district nurses have an enormous and valuable reservoir of information about older people and their needs.

48. Half the population over 85 are seen by district nursing services each year and district nurses have an enormous and valuable reservoir of information about older people and their needs. But district nurses' potential to contribute to community health needs assessment is seldom realised. More than half the district nurses surveyed by the Audit Commission said that their teams were not involved in profiling the health needs of their local community.

49. In practice, the only available measure of need is expressed demand, as measured by referrals, and these are subject to all kinds of influence. For example, some GPs are known to refer patients to the district nursing service when they are uncertain whom else to refer to, or when they suspect that referral to other services will result in delay.

50. Referral rates (from all sources) vary between populations. In one trust, people were four times more likely to be referred to district nursing from the highest referring practice populations than from the lowest [EXHIBIT 8]. Explanations for these variations include practice age profile; deprivation levels; the organisation of nursing staff. But differences in the clinical behaviour of referrers are also important.

51. Large variations in referral rates between similar populations suggest that the referral system is an inadequate means of identifying need. Whether a patient is referred to the district nursing service is largely dictated by individual referrers' views as to what constitutes need and what needs can be met by district nursing. In practice, when faced with vulnerable individuals, district nurses tend to be accommodating, delivering care to people even if they believe those needs would, in the long term, be better provided by other services.

EXHIBIT 8

Referral rates to district nursing by GP practice population size

There is a fourfold variation in the referral rates to the district nursing service across GP practices.

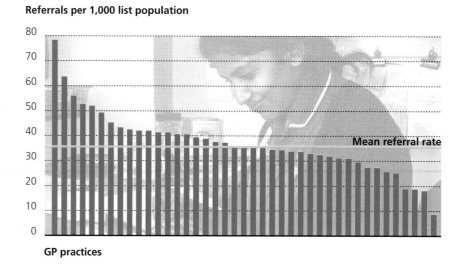

Referrals per 1,000 list population

Mean referral rate

GP practices

Source: Audit Commission study site

52. If those referring have a broad understanding of district nursing, they are more likely to refer patients for a district nursing assessment (Ref. 17). This kind of referral should be encouraged since it enables district nurses to use their professional judgement to determine appropriate nursing care and to initiate and co-ordinate input from other services. But only one in five referrals in the Audit Commission's survey were for assessment.[17]

53. Where referrers have a poorer understanding of district nursing, their more limited knowledge of the services that district nurses can provide means that they tend to refer a narrower range of patients for a restricted set of clinical tasks. Eighty per cent of referrals captured by the Audit Commission's survey were task-oriented [**EXHIBIT 9**], the largest number being for wound checks, dressings and venepuncture.

54. Trusts, with health authorities and the new PCGs/LHGs, should be exploiting district nurses' potential to undertake community needs assessment, looking at the configuration of services and service providers and deciding, in the context of local health improvement programmes (HImPs), what needs they want the district nursing service to meet.

EXHIBIT 9

Referral to district nursing by reason

Most referrals are task-oriented reflecting a poor understanding of district nursing services.

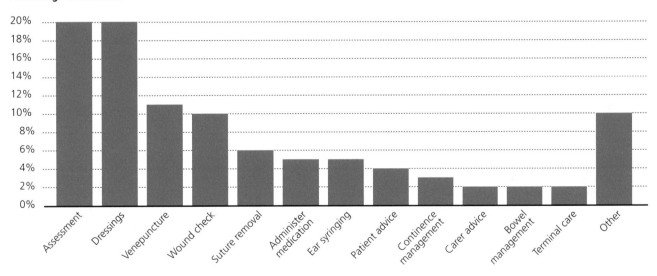

Percentage of referrals

Reason for referral

Source: Audit Commission referral surveys

District nursing teams may also be unable to meet identified needs because of failings in other services.

55. Several different types of need can be distinguished.

- First, there are unidentified needs in the community for the types of nursing care that district nurses can provide.[18] Existing needs may not be recognised at a sufficiently early stage in a patient's illness and patients may not be referred to district nurses until a crisis occurs. With half of those over 75 now living alone, and most of the remainder with elderly carers, there is a real question of who provides nursing care when, for example, they have flu or a serious stomach upset. Short-term illnesses such as these can trigger more serious problems that lead to hospital admission. District nurses report that prompt referral of patients with a terminal or chronic illness would enable advice and support for patients and carers to be provided earlier.

- Second, there are identified needs that district nursing teams are unable to meet because of the need to prioritise. As district nursing teams have an increasing role in providing care for very elderly patients and for patients with increasingly complex needs, their ability to care for less dependent patients may be diminished. It is not clear that the needs of these patients are now met elsewhere. District nursing teams may also be unable to meet identified needs because of failings in other services. For example, where the provision of aids to daily living is inadequate, patients (and carers) may be more dependent on district nursing services as a result.

- Third, there are patients whose needs for nursing care are currently met elsewhere (in hospital or hospice) but which could be provided more suitably, and possibly more cheaply,[19] by district nurses at home [CASE STUDY 1 and Appendix 5]. Some are already patients of the district nursing service but receive part of their care in a hospital setting. For example, in a few trusts district nurses provide complex treatments at home, such as intravenous cytotoxic therapy or blood transfusion services.

56. The additional funds made available in October 1997 through the Winter Pressures Money and the Continuing Care Challenge Fund have demonstrated that, where resources are made available, district nurses, working with social services, can address some of these different types of need. These schemes[20] include:

- Shropshire: a rapid response home care team in which district nurses and home care workers worked closely together to provide care at home and to avert a crisis for individuals. Health and social services plan to continue the scheme in urban areas during 1998/99 using joint finance.

- Leicestershire: peripatetic community nursing teams provided an estimated 18,000 hours of extra nursing support for night services, helping to relieve pressure on hospital admissions and to develop healthcare packages. A discharge co-ordinator post promoted better working with social services and other care providers.

- South and West Devon: a project was set up which aimed to reduce unnecessary admissions through quick assessment and easy access to rehabilitation. This included free admission to nursing homes for 72 hours and co-ordinated access to health and social services.

57. Commissioning by PCGs/LHGs may offer opportunities, and incentives, that encourage community trusts to form innovative new services and for such schemes to become a core part of the service.

CASE STUDY 1

The Bolton Rapid Response Team

Community Healthcare Bolton NHS Trust introduced a rapid response team in September 1995. This extension to the normal district nursing service comprises a team of nursing and therapy staff. Its primary aim is to provide a direct alternative to acute hospital admission by giving the necessary level of support for patients in their own home for up to 14 days.

The types of patient who are suitable for admission to the rapid response team include:

- patients suffering from acute illness who can be managed at home by the multidisciplinary team;

- individuals with severe disabilities who have an acute episode (for example, acute infection, falls) which affects their carers' ability to cope; and

- patients being cared for at home who need more palliative care than can be provided by the district nursing and Marie Curie services.

Referrals from GPs, hospital consultants, district nurses, social services and others are made to the team co-ordinator who assesses the patient within two to four hours in collaboration with the district nursing sister. The team (five wte F grades; five wte B grade healthcare support workers; 0.6 wte G grade team co-ordinator; one wte physiotherapist, 12 hours of occupational therapy and one clerical officer) can accommodate up to 15 patients. In 1997/98 the service received 379 referrals.

With a budget (1998/99) of £257,000, the scheme was expanded in late 1997 to provide additional support to the A&E department and the medical assessment unit of the local hospital trust. These patients will have received a full medical assessment and be deemed medically stable but may require immediate input from community nursing and/or therapists which, if not provided, would result in hospital admission.

The main benefit of the scheme is its ability to improve the quality of life – or death – for patients, and to provide support for carers. Early evaluation also suggests significant cost benefits. The average cost of £637 per finished episode (based on a five-day stay – although this is falling) compares with the cost of hospital inpatient stay of £200 per day. The scheme also provides for early discharge and rehabilitation for some patients. For example, anterior cruxiate ligament repair can be treated as day surgery at an average cost in the community of £88.35 per completed patient episode, compared with the costs of a five-day hospital stay.

Source: Audit Commission study site

Sources of referral

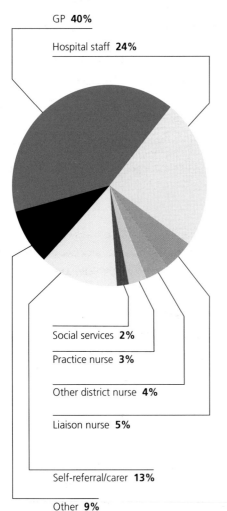

GP **40%**

Hospital staff **24%**

Social services **2%**

Practice nurse **3%**

Other district nurse **4%**

Liaison nurse **5%**

Self-referral/carer **13%**

Other **9%**

Source: Audit Commission referral surveys

58. District nurses depend on others, particularly GPs and hospital staff (including liaison nurses), to recognise that a person needs district nursing care and to refer appropriately. Seven out of every ten referrals come from these two sources; but in most places, GPs are the primary gatekeepers to district nursing [EXHIBIT 10].

59. On average, two-fifths of referrals are made by GPs. But in some trusts, this figure can be closer to two-thirds. And referral rates vary considerably between GP practices and between GPs within practices (Ref. 17). On average, 29 per cent of referrals to district nursing come from hospitals. But in some trusts, this is as high as 45 per cent.

60. The public has limited information about the service [CASE HISTORY C] and the share of referrals coming from patients or carers varies widely between trusts. In some, almost one-quarter of referrals are from patients, in others it is fewer than 5 per cent. Generally, the number of self-referrals has remained static and a high proportion (up to half) of such referrals are made by (or on behalf of) people who have previously been in receipt of district nursing.

61. Despite the increased role of social services in the assessment of need since the implementation of the NHS and Community Care Act in 1993, and the fact that they largely share the same client group, comparatively few referrals (between 1 and 4 per cent) are made by social services staff. This low referral rate may reflect a restricted view of district nurses' roles, which would not be surprising given that most social services' staff have only limited contact with district nurses and opportunities for joint discussion are rare. Where social workers are GP-attached, and in some cases practice-based, better opportunities for formal and informal contact can improve their understanding of the district nursing role and the development of co-operative working practices (Ref. 18).

CASE HISTORY C

This 47-year-old man is looking after his wife who has multiple sclerosis. He sold his business about five years ago to become her full-time carer when her condition began to deteriorate. He cared for her on his own for some time before district nursing and social services got involved. She had become doubly incontinent, developed a pressure sore on the base of her spine, and her weight had fallen to five-and-a-half stone. He was carrying her up to bed, and back down in the morning. He didn't call for help because *'I mean, who do you turn to, where do you turn to? I wasn't in the know, so gradually I packed up work and we coped as best we could.'*

His wife was admitted to hospital and a care package set up for her return home. She has been unable to move at all over the last few months, and is now on drip feeds. Two carers come in twice a day to help with washing and dressing. The district nurses come in about once a week, and telephone regularly to see if she needs a visit. They have also organised respite care for her husband.

Source: Audit Commission patients' and carers' study

Problems with the referral process

62. Referral will always be the main means of identifying individual patients' need for district nursing. It is important that the process works well, but in many cases it does not. Two main areas of concern are examined here:

- some patients are being referred inappropriately; and
- the information that is provided at the time of referral is inadequate.

These problems are common to referrals from all sources. Other problems arise when patients are being transferred from hospital to community care; these are also examined here.

Inappropriate referral

63. The vast majority of referrals are judged to be appropriate by district nurses. But one in ten were considered inappropriate. This proportion varied from 6 per cent to 11 per cent across the study sites. In part, this variation reflects the lack of consistency over service objectives. In some trusts, district nurses describe referrals as inappropriate if, following assessment, there is no ongoing need for nursing. But, in other trusts – where it is accepted that a major part of the district nurses' role is to promote health and independence, and that assessment includes giving advice, information and onward referral – the same referrals would be considered appropriate.

In some areas, one in four referrals was incomplete...

64. Referrals that are inappropriate may waste district nursing resources, chiefly in assessment, and risk delaying the delivery of more appropriate services to the individual. In assessment time alone, inappropriate referrals cost the average trust £22,000 per year, the equivalent of a G grade salary.[21] But in some cases the costs are much higher because district nurses provide ongoing support until other services are in place. The Audit Commission's survey found that district nurses planned to revisit more than one-fifth of the patients they had identified as inappropriately referred.

65. District nurses gave three main reasons for judging a referral to be inappropriate:

- the referral should have gone to a practice nurse, a GP or to social services;

- the patient should not have been discharged from hospital because appropriate services and support were not in place; and

- no nursing care was required.

66. Inappropriate referrals often come from only a handful of GPs or from particular hospital wards. For example, at one study site trust, two GP practices accounted for more than half of the referrals that district nurses thought were inappropriate. Inappropriate referrals cannot be entirely eliminated – to do so would require referrers to have a consistent and highly accurate awareness of what constitutes need for district nursing. But if some trusts have low rates, others can too. As a first step, trusts need to identify where inappropriate referrals originate.

Poor referral information

67. It is important that the information provided at the time of referral is as complete as possible. Sometimes the most basic information – for example, telling the district nurse how to gain access to the patient's home or that the patient has communication difficulties – is missing. The failure to provide all the relevant information can lead to abortive or ineffective visits and to delays in care delivery.

68. Overall, the information provided by nearly one in five referrals was considered to be inadequate by district nurses [EXHIBIT 11]. The extent of the problem varies within and between trusts. In some areas, one in four referrals was deemed incomplete by district nurses. In part, this variation reflects the methods used to refer patients and the sources of referral. Referrals left on telephone answering machines were particularly prone to omitting important information. And one-quarter of all referrals from hospital staff (including discharge liaison nurses) were considered to be inadequate by district nurses.

EXHIBIT 11

Inadequate referrals by source

The information that district nurses receive is inadequate in 20 per cent of cases.

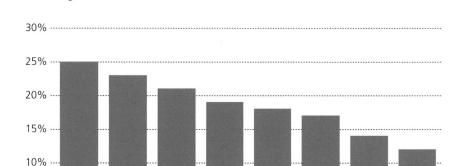

Percentage of referrals

Source of referrals

Source: Audit Commission referral surveys

69. Almost one in ten referrals provided incorrect or misleading information about the patient's condition. Other common failings included incorrect patient details; no information on equipment needs (for example, moving and handling equipment) or medication prescribed; no information about the patient's mobility or their mental health; and no information on whether the patient was aware of their diagnosis. The need for trusts to encourage better referral information may require them to identify those referrers that consistently provide poor information and work with them to improve referrals.

Problems with hospital referrals

70. Reductions in the length of hospital stay and an increase in the dependency levels of patients who are discharged to the community have increased the need for effective discharge planning. But poorly planned hospital discharges and poor communication between hospital and community nursing staff prior to discharge can result in patients being sent home inappropriately and not receiving the services they need (Refs. 19, 20 and 21). The consequences can be slower rehabilitation and recovery and, in the worst cases, deterioration in the patient's condition and hospital readmission. Problems with hospital referral commonly highlighted by district nurses include:

- the absence of basic patient information, such as details of their illness or medication;

- inappropriately referred patients who are mobile and could be seen by a practice nurse or in a district nurse clinic;

- lack of sufficient notice to arrange services, particularly at weekends;

...trusts have tried to improve co-ordination between hospital and community services by employing liaison nurses.

- giving patients or carers expectations that district nursing cannot meet;

- lack of essential supplies being sent home with the patient; and

- advising the patient to contact district nursing if they have a problem while failing to inform district nurses that the patient has been discharged.

71. Many trusts have tried to improve co-ordination between hospital and community services by employing liaison nurses.[22] But it is not clear that liaison nurses are reducing the level of problematic discharges from hospital. The Audit Commission's survey showed no differences in the proportions of referrals that were judged to be inappropriate between trusts with a liaison nurse service and those without. This confirms the view that, where they are seen as the formal channel of communication, discharge liaison nurses may actually reinforce barriers between community-based and hospital-based staff (Ref. 22). The presence of a liaison nurse may discourage ward staff from taking responsibility for discharge planning and for learning about local services.

72. The Audit Commission's survey of referrals to liaison nurses found that 20 per cent of patients who had been in hospital for more than three weeks were referred to the liaison nurse only on the day of their discharge. When patients are referred to them this late, liaison nurses seldom have enough time to co-ordinate care effectively. Clinical audit needs to highlight the problems that arise and then identify appropriate solutions.

Improving the referral process

73. The referral process would be more accurate, effective and efficient if the service had referral criteria and referral pathways. Usable guidelines on referral depend, in turn, on having a clear definition of the service and its purpose. Trusts could take relatively simple steps to identify where inappropriate referrals originate and provide those referrers with clearer guidance. They also need to encourage better referral information through, for example, the use of standardised checklists or forms to help those taking referrals. The development of electronic patient records and electronic health records could also help to improve referral in the community (Ref.16).

74. In the case of referral from hospital, more innovative solutions might be required. These could involve, for example, rotating hospital nurses into the community for a short spell, running in-service training on discharge planning and on nursing in the community, or basing liaison nurses in the community [CASE STUDY 2]. The concept of rotation is one idea that would benefit from further research. If liaison nurses are to be part of the solution, they need to have clear, realistic objectives and a system for monitoring performance against these objectives. Rather than being the person who plans hospital discharge, they need to establish frameworks for liaison between services, helping ward and community staff to form more appropriate local arrangements.

CASE STUDY 2

Community liaison nurse post

In some trusts, liaison nurses are community-based. In 1996, West Lindsey NHS Trust worked with a four-practice total-purchasing pilot in a part of Lincolnshire where local hospitals had no discharge planning co-ordinators or liaison nurses, to introduce a community liaison nurse post. The aim of the post was to:

- reduce the number of inappropriate discharges through liaison with hospital staff; and
- reduce the number of postponed operations through pre-admission screening.

Initially, community liaison nurses visited all patients over the age of 60 who were waiting for elective admission and all emergency admissions, irrespective of diagnosis or ward. The role has been extended to cover elective admissions for major surgery, irrespective of the patient's age. The benefits of pre-admission screening include:

- patients are as fit as possible before surgery;
- patients are not sent home unexpectedly after admission when problems are highlighted at the last moment; and
- timely postponement of admissions ensures that the hospital waiting list is managed more effectively.

Potential post-discharge needs are identified and recorded on an assessment form that accompanies the patient into hospital. The liaison nurse visits the patients in hospital and liaises with ward staff to discuss discharge arrangements. Patients are followed up after discharge from hospital in order to determine their level of satisfaction with discharge arrangements, and to identify post-discharge problems such as wound infection or insufficient supplies of medications or dressings. Evaluation has demonstrated that both the number of inappropriate discharges and the number of operations postponed has declined.

Source: Audit Commission trust visit

Managing caseloads to improve efficiency

75. District nursing is a highly responsive service, reacting promptly to the receipt of referral information. Most referrals (80 per cent) are followed up within 24 hours. But district nurses have little control over admissions to their caseload and, as a consequence, manage their workloads by juggling, sometimes on a daily basis, the frequency or duration of their visits and discharge decisions. This method of management does not promote safe and effective practice. Practitioners and managers must give more detailed attention to prioritising visits [CASE STUDY 3] and actively managing caseloads.

CASE STUDY 3

Patient priority criteria

Some trusts have developed guidelines to help district nurses to prioritise patient visits. Nurses are expected to make evidence-based judgements and to apply the criteria flexibly. Typically, there are three categories:

Priority 1

- New referrals
- Assessments
- Essential clinical visits: insulin-dependent diabetic patients; patients needing bowel/bladder management; patients relying on nurses to administer medication; patients requiring dressings daily or three times a week
- Palliative care
- Priority 2 patients whose visits have been postponed once
- Priority 3 patients whose visits have been postponed twice

Priority 2

- Clinical visits (dressings, catheter care, bowel care, support) to patients who require twice-weekly care may be postponed to the next day, at which point they become Priority 1 patients

Priority 3

- Reassessment for incontinence aids
- Monitoring visits
- Clinical visits which are scheduled weekly or less frequently

Visits in this category become Priority 1 after two postponements.

Source: Croydon Health Authority

76. District nurses are responsible for managing the care of widely varying numbers of patients. The caseloads reviewed by the Audit Commission ranged from fewer than 20 to more than 40 patients[23] per wte team member [**EXHIBIT 12**]. This wide variation raises questions about whether resources are allocated equitably and whether patients have equity of access.

77. But the workload generated by a particular caseload does not depend on the number of patients alone. The extent of carer support for patients and the numbers of unsupported, dependent patients on the caseload are also important. These, and other factors, influence the frequency with which patients are seen, the amount of nurses' time that each patient contact requires, and the intensity of patients' needs. Some teams see most of their patients at least once a week, while others see half their patients less than once a month [**EXHIBIT 13, overleaf**]. Patients who are seen infrequently have limited impact on the total workload, but trusts should consider whether the care delivered to these patients is needed and whether resources could be used more effectively.

78. Generally, the more patients on the caseload, the less frequent the contact [**EXHIBIT 14, overleaf**]. But there is considerable variation. For example, at 40 patients per wte, the proportion of patients seen infrequently (once per month or less) ranges from 35 per cent to 70 per cent. This variation raises questions about how nurses are spending their time and the extent to which trusts are able to deploy additional resources to ease workloads if, for example, a team has an influx of highly dependent patients.

EXHIBIT 12

Number of patients on the caseload per wte team member

Workloads measured simply as numbers of patients vary fivefold between different teams.

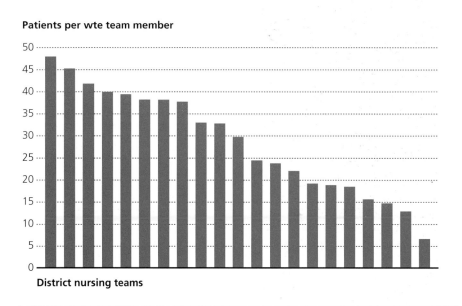

Patients per wte team member

District nursing teams

Source: Audit Commission caseload reviews

EXHIBIT 13

Frequency of patient contact by team

Some teams see half their patients less than once a month.

Percentage of patients

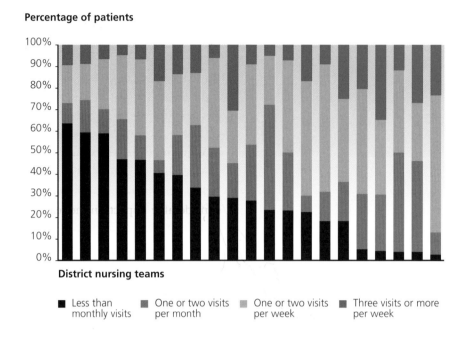

District nursing teams

- ■ Less than monthly visits
- ■ One or two visits per month
- ■ One or two visits per week
- ■ Three visits or more per week

Source: Audit Commission caseload reviews

EXHIBIT 14

Frequency of visits by number of patients per wte

Generally, the more patients on the caseload, the less frequent the visits.

Percentage of patients receiving visits monthly or less frequently

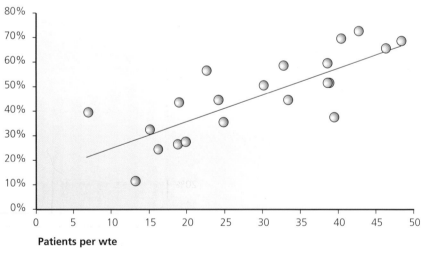

Patients per wte

○ **District nursing teams**

Note: r^2 = 0.6209

Source: Audit Commission caseload reviews

Measuring dependence

79. It is possible to measure the dependency of patients on the district nursing team in a standardised way. Analysis of caseloads using a validated tool[24] explicitly designed for use in the community shows that the majority (85 per cent) of patients have low dependency on the district nursing team [**EXHIBIT 15**], with one in ten patients scoring the minimum possible.[25] Only 1 per cent of patients were classified as being highly dependent on the district nursing team. But these patients are consistently visited more frequently than others: 86 per cent are seen three or more times a week, including 67 per cent who are seen daily or more than once a day. Having only one or two highly dependent patients can have a considerable impact on the team's workload.

Discharging patients

80. Turnover on some nurses' caseloads is greater than others. For some teams, more than half the patients have been 'on the books' for two or more years while, in others, more than half have been on the caseload for less than six months [**EXHIBIT 16, overleaf**]. These variations may reflect differences in the casemix – patients staying on the caseload for long periods are likely to have complex health needs resulting from chronic conditions. Variations may also reflect the fact that some areas have better organised services to which to refer patients once they have been discharged from hospital.

EXHIBIT 15

Patient dependency on district nursing by team

One per cent of patients are highly dependent on the district nursing team.

Percentage of patients

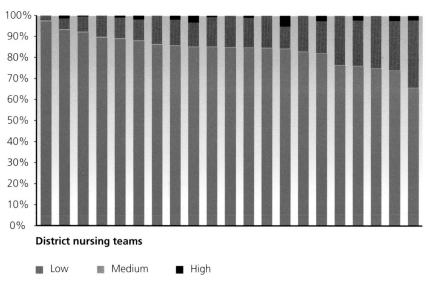

District nursing teams

■ Low   ■ Medium   ■ High

Source: Audit Commission caseload reviews

EXHIBIT 16

Length of time on the caseload by team

Some nurses keep patients on their caseloads longer than others do.

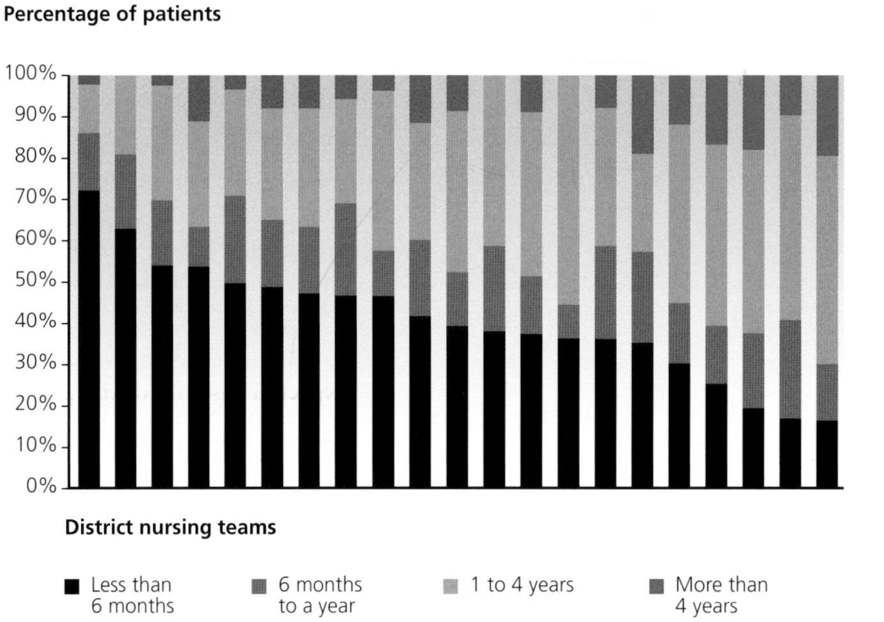

Percentage of patients

District nursing teams

- Less than 6 months
- 6 months to a year
- 1 to 4 years
- More than 4 years

Source: Audit Commission caseload reviews

81. Discharging patients from district nursing care is not always straightforward and district nurses may face a number of dilemmas.[26] They may be reluctant to discharge patients if they feel that appropriate social care arrangements are not in place. Some district nurses argue that it is better to retain particularly vulnerable patients on their caseloads, and provide a monthly 'observation' visit giving them the opportunity to intervene early, rather than discharge them, only to re-admit them a few months later when a crisis arises. But the addition of new terminally ill, or highly dependent, patients to a caseload can make this approach difficult. Rather than discharging patients to cope with the new workload, district nurses tend to vary the frequency of visits to existing patients.

82. In many cases, the process of discharge is one of graduated withdrawal in which the frequency of district nurses' visits diminishes over time. This approach to discharge, often poorly articulated on care plans, may be designed to build up patient (and/or carer) confidence while reassuring the nurse that standards of care are being maintained or that measures to prevent recurrence are being followed (Ref. 23). Sometimes district nurses continue to visit unofficially ('popping back') after discharge – for example, continuing to visit a relative some time after the patient has died or visiting former patients where a particularly close attachment has been formed.

...there was little evidence that managers use caseload profiling to inform decision-making...

Caseload profiling

83. The district nurse is responsible for reviewing individual patient cases on a regular basis: at case conferences, when planning visits and at each patient encounter. However, only rarely do district nurses systematically and regularly profile their whole caseload by:

- comparing the numbers of patients on teams' 'active' caseloads;
- profiling the age, gender, frequency of visits, care packages and dependency on the nursing team of the whole caseload;
- estimating the workload generated by a particular casemix; and
- comparing the caseload at a practice level in terms of the size and expected casemix of the practice list.

84. In study sites, there was little evidence that managers use caseload profiling to inform decision-making. One trust, however, has started formally reviewing caseloads every three to six months, which involves examining the numbers of patients, frequency of visits, patient condition and other factors. The introduction of a regular review process, including dependency measurement, is reported to have reduced the numbers of patients on caseloads by encouraging more regular discharge or transfer to more suitable care provision by social services or voluntary organisations [CASE STUDY 4, overleaf].

85. In addition to ensuring that caseload profiling takes place, trust managers should be actively setting limits to protect standards. At one study site a district nursing team could, in consultation with the nurse manager and the GPs, temporarily close its caseload to new patients when it became 'full'. A caseload would be deemed 'full' when accepting further referrals would restrict the delivery of care to other patients as well as to the newly referred patient, even after rescheduling any visits that could be postponed. Patients referred to a team with a full caseload would, temporarily, be passed on to another team for their nursing care. The manager would then liaise with potential referrers and monitor the situation in conjunction with the district nurse and the GPs. This procedure was seldom invoked.

CASE STUDY 4

Using caseload review

West Lindsey NHS Trust used the opportunity, which arose when a G grade post became vacant in Gainsborough, to review the relationship between resources and patient needs. The Trust used the dependency tool (para. 79) as part of an exercise to profile the caseloads of the five district nursing teams working with 14 local GPs in two practices. Although district nurses worked geographically, and the five teams were based only two miles apart, there was little communication between them and a failure to share dependent patients.

The characteristics – the type of nursing care provided, primary reason for care, and the number of visits – of each caseload were taken from the patient activity system and the dependency of patients on the district nursing team established. Only 5 per cent of patients were categorised as highly dependent on the district nursing teams, but nearly half of these patients (most of whom had cancer) were on one caseload. Two caseholders had no high-dependency patients. In 45 per cent of cases, the primary reason for district nursing care was urinary incontinence and all incontinent patients were being seen at home. As a result of the exercise, caseloads and resources were realigned and a district-nurse-run continence clinic was established.

As well as assessing the dependency of the patient at the start of an episode of care and contributing to caseload profiling, the dependency tool has been used to:

- prioritise visits – visits to some patients may need to be cancelled to meet unexpected peaks in workload. The tool helps nurses to decide which, if any, visits can be postponed and for how long. Visits to patients categorised as high dependency may not be postponed, whereas visits to low-dependency patients can be postponed up to three times;

- justify requests for bank nurses – where the patients being visited are categorised as high-dependency; and

- ensure that patients are appropriately placed in nursing or residential care – some patients placed in residential homes were categorised as high-dependency and judged to have been inappropriately placed. Social services has now agreed to accept the dependency scores as part of joint assessments before arranging nursing or residential care.

Source: Audit Commission trust visit

86. Regular profiling of caseloads can help district nurses and trust managers to improve their efficiency by ensuring that resources are targeted at those with greatest need [BOX D]. And it would also help trusts to challenge sometimes rigid GP attachment and argue for allocating resources to practices more objectively and more flexibly. All of these issues are relevant to improving the delivery of district nursing services. Their importance is becoming even greater as PCGs/LHGs form and the question of how services are purchased and resourced moves on to the PCG/LHG agenda.

87. To facilitate effective caseload monitoring, individual caseload holders need access to accurate and reliable patient data. Even within the same trust, not all district nurses have ready access to the patient information system – in part because they may be based in GP premises which are not integrated with the trust's information systems and in part because of a lack of investment in information systems (Ref. 16).

BOX D

Benefits of caseload profiling

By improving their information on district nurses' caseloads and how they use it, trusts will be better placed to:

• encourage patient discharge and the transfer of their care to more suitable services, where appropriate;

• encourage district nurses to monitor their own caseloads;

• regularly monitor changes in casemix for individual caseloads;

• use this information on casemix to estimate the workload generated by a particular caseload and adjust resource allocation if necessary;

• compare caseload profiles to practice and population profiles and investigate any anomalies;

• identify the types of care that patients are receiving and shape them into 'care packages';

• develop sets of core competencies for the assessment and delivery of packages of care;

• match staff skills to these competencies (for example, train more nurses in the skills needed to deliver terminal care packages if the number of patients receiving this package is increasing); and

• discuss with purchasers the possibility of developing a future contracting currency based on 'packages of care' rather than simply on the number of contacts.

RECOMMENDATIONS

2 Managing Demand for District Nursing Services

Trusts, with commissioners, need to define the objectives and role of the service by:

1 agreeing, with district nurses, clear service objectives

2 working with PCGs/LHGs to adopt a more proactive approach to identifying need at the community and practice levels

3 increasing public awareness of what the service can offer and enabling more patients and carers to have direct access to the service

Trusts need to influence and manage demand better by:

4 producing criteria for referrals and communicating these to GPs and other potential referrers

5 developing a clear checklist of information required from referrers and targeting those who refer inappropriately or inadequately

6 working together (that is, community and hospital trusts) to institute a thorough review of discharge and establishing options for improving liaison

Efficiency and effectiveness could be improved if trusts:

7 ensured that assessments set a target discharge or review date

8 reviewed district nurses' caseloads on a regular basis to encourage discharge and transfer of care to other services

9 instituted the use of patient dependency tools to monitor and review casemix and resourcing

Improving the Quality of Care

Evaluating quality is difficult when defining good care is seldom clear cut. But patients' treatment can suffer when the quality of assessment is not monitored and evidence about effectiveness is not introduced systematically. In order to improve the quality of care, trusts need effective systems for monitoring current practice and for translating research on good practice into daily use.

Introduction

Some patients have poorer outcomes than they should...

88. Caring for people with complex and multiple needs – the chronically ill and the terminally ill – calls for thorough and comprehensive assessment, for judgements about how and when to involve others in providing care, for knowledge about other services and how to orchestrate them to meet patients' needs. Evaluating performance on any of these dimensions is difficult since determining what constitutes 'good care' is seldom clear cut and there are comparatively few outcome measures that can be used to gauge the standards of care. As a proxy, we can examine some of the key processes that contribute to the quality of care and look at the outcomes in terms of users' experiences of the service.

89. This chapter uses two conditions – leg ulcers and incontinence – as 'probe' conditions. These were selected because of their prevalence, their prominence in district nurses' caseloads, their costs to the NHS, and the existence of evidence-based clinical practice guidelines [BOX E]. In both cases, comprehensive, accurate assessment is acknowledged as a major determinant of successful patient outcomes and the chapter focuses on assessment as a key indicator of good quality care.

90. In order to improve quality of care, trusts need to have effective systems for monitoring practice and for translating good practice evidence into daily use. The probes are used to examine how these systems currently operate. Some patients have poorer outcomes than they should because assessment quality is not monitored, evidence about effectiveness is not systematically introduced and outcomes are poorly evaluated. With appropriate infrastructure and support, clinical nurse specialists can play a key role in improving these practices. But the ways in which these nurses are deployed, and the resources available to them, sometimes inhibit their performance.

91. It is important that services focus on the needs of patients and carers and that their views are taken into account in service planning. This chapter uses interviews with leg ulcer and continence patients, and their carers, to examine what is important about district nursing from the users' perspective.

92. Although the problems described here are specific to leg ulcer and continence patients, other conditions would raise the same general issues. There is little evidence that trusts provide ongoing training to nursing staff on the use of assessment documentation and tools, and even less evidence that the quality of the assessments which are conducted is subject to effective peer review or audit. As a result, problems of poor clinical performance may go unrecognised.

BOX E

Leg ulcers and incontinence: key characteristics

LEG ULCERS

Leg ulcers are areas of skin loss below the knee on the leg or foot which take more than six weeks to heal. The major types, and causes, of leg ulceration are:

- venous leg ulcers – about 70 per cent of leg ulcers are the result of poor blood flow from the legs back to the heart;
- arterial leg ulcers – about 10 per cent of leg ulcers form when there is reduced blood flow to the arteries in the lower leg. This is usually caused by fatty deposits which narrow the artery;
- mixed (venous and arterial) aetiology ulcers – account for between 10 per cent and 15 per cent of ulcers; and
- more unusual causes (up to 5 per cent) such as diabetic ulcers (generally on the foot); rheumatoid arthritis; malignancy; blood disorders (sickle cell anaemia; thalassaemia) and lymphoedema.

Leg ulcers pose a significant challenge for the health service in general and for district nursing in particular. Estimates suggest that 400,000 people in the UK suffer from leg ulceration, of whom 25 per cent require treatment at any one time. Prevalence increases with age and affects twice as many women as men. Two-thirds of patients experience two or more episodes of ulceration.

The annual cost to the NHS of treating leg ulceration has been estimated (1992 prices) at £236 million[27] (Ref. 24). Nursing staff costs are the major component of expenditure. It is likely that this cost will rise as the number of elderly people increases. The majority of patients are treated in community settings and district nurses are generally the leading contributors to care. Estimates suggest that leg ulcer patients contribute up to 20 per cent of district nurses' workload and account for up to half of their patient contact time. Considerable variation in clinical practice and outcomes is reported.

INCONTINENCE

Incontinence is defined as *'the involuntary loss of urine or faeces which may be demonstrated objectively'* (Ref. 25). The main causes of incontinence include:

- weak pelvic floor muscles (for example, following childbirth) leading to leakage (stress incontinence);
- an overactive bladder (causing frequency and urge incontinence);
- difficulty emptying the bladder (for example, because of an enlarged prostate) leading to dribbling overflow incontinence;
- neurological conditions – for example, dementia or multiple sclerosis;
- constipation and other bowel problems; and
- any difficulty in reaching the toilet, such as physical disability, confusion, an inaccessible toilet or unavailable carer.

Accurate estimates of the prevalence of urinary and faecal incontinence are not readily available. But over three million people in Britain are thought to have a continence problem. A review by the Royal College of Physicians (Ref. 25) estimates that, at age 65 and over, 10-20 per cent of women and 7-10 per cent of men have urinary incontinence. The reported prevalence of faecal incontinence is 3-5 per cent of those aged 65 to 84 and 15 per cent of those aged 85 and over.

The financial cost of incontinence is unknown but estimates made in 1991 suggest that the NHS spends between £50 and £60 million per year on continence products alone (Ref. 26).* Research suggests that up to 70 per cent of people who present with incontinence can be successfully treated. The remainder may not regain full control, but their incontinence can be managed and district nurses are, for adults at least, the main contributors to care.

More recently, the Continence Foundation has suggested that NHS expenditure on absorbent products is in excess of £120 million a year.

Leg ulcer assessment

The main determinant of successful leg ulcer management is thorough assessment.

93. A recent *Effective Health Care Bulletin* concluded: *'There is widespread variation in practice, and evidence of unnecessary suffering and costs due to inadequate management of venous leg ulcers in the community'* (Ref. 27). The main determinant of successful leg ulcer management is a thorough assessment and accurate diagnosis of the underlying cause, combined with appropriate treatment and the prevention of recurrence. The importance of comprehensive and accurate assessment of patients is highlighted by the fact that compression bandaging, the principal intervention for patients with venous leg ulcers, can lead to considerable damage in patients with arterial leg ulcers.

Recommended practice

94. A new clinical practice guideline for the management of patients with venous leg ulcers has been published (Ref. 28). The guidelines enumerate key items of information that have a bearing on the accurate identification of underlying causes, appropriate treatment, the progress and monitoring of healing, pain control, the need for specialist referral and the likelihood of recurrence. This information should be part of a comprehensive assessment for every patient with a leg ulcer.

95. At each of the Audit Commission's seven study site trusts, assessment documentation was reviewed for a sample of between 17 and 25 new patients who had been assessed in the previous six months. Each assessment was compared against a checklist of items [BOX F] based on the guidelines on recommended practice, and a percentage completion score was derived from the results.

Quality of assessments

96. The quality of assessment for patients with leg ulcers varies widely between trusts. More than three-quarters of the assessment items were completed at the best performing trust compared with less than one-quarter at the poorest [EXHIBIT 17].

97. Where similar audits have been conducted by trusts, they have shown widely varying performance by district nursing teams. Trusts can use this kind of audit information to target training and specialist advice, but it is often not available.

BOX F

Components of a comprehensive leg ulcer assessment

GENERAL	LEG ULCERS	LEG HEALTH	OTHER
Age	Type of ulcer	Conditions of the legs/feet	Referral to specialist nurse
Gender	Site(s) of ulcer(s)	Skin integrity surrounding the leg ulcer	Referral to medical clinician
Medical history	Date of onset	Skin integrity of the legs	Referral to other health professionals
History of venous disease	Recurrence of leg ulcer	Measurement of pedal pulses	Routine clinical investigations[28]
History of arterial disease	Events surrounding the onset	General circulation of feet	
Medications	Size of ulcer	Doppler ultrasound	
Allergies	Depth of ulcer		
Mobility	Appearance of ulcer		
Nutritional state	Odour		
Smoking habits	Pain		
Psychological health			
Understanding of health needs			
Lifestyle/social activities			

EXHIBIT 17

Completion scores for leg ulcer assessments by trust

The quality of assessment for patients with leg ulcers varies between trusts.

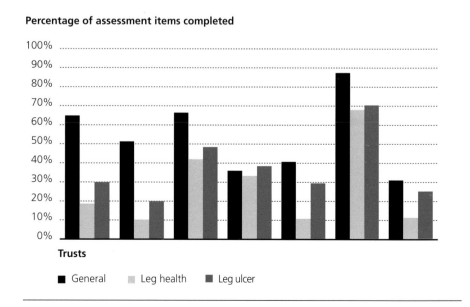

Percentage of assessment items completed

Trusts

■ General ▨ Leg health ■ Leg ulcer

Source: Audit Commission reviews of assessment documentation

98. When the percentage completion scores are broken down into their component parts [EXHIBIT 18] the extent of the variation becomes even more apparent. Some of the recommended elements of leg ulcer assessment are often missing. For example:

- patients with venous leg ulcers are often allergic to commonly used products containing lanolin and topical antibiotics. It is important to identify such sensitivity so as to avoid these products. On average, only half the assessments contained information on allergies; completion varied from 16 per cent in the worst case to 96 per cent in the best;

- all patients should be given the benefit of Doppler ultrasound to measure the ankle/brachial pressure index (ABPI) in screening for arterial disease and referral to specialist vascular clinics. But only half the patients had a Doppler ultrasound reading recorded. In one trust, fewer than one in six assessments indicated a Doppler score;[29] and

- practitioners should regularly monitor whether patients experience pain associated with their leg ulcer(s). Pain may be a sign of underlying pathology such as arterial insufficiency or infection, and uncontrolled pain can lead to a cycle of ulcer deterioration.[30] The Audit Commission review found very variable patterns of recording. Overall, fewer than half the assessments made any reference to pain and in three trusts fewer than one-quarter did.

Continence assessment

99. Assessment is of prime importance for the appropriate management and promotion of continence. In 1998, a new clinical audit scheme for the management of urinary and faecal incontinence was produced by the Royal College of Physicians (Ref. 29). The audit provides a comprehensive checklist of good practice designed to establish:

- the cause of incontinence;

- the investigations and treatment required;

- how the objectives of treatment can be met; and

- how the patient can achieve the best quality of life.

EXHIBIT 18

EXHIBIT 18

Completion scores for leg ulcer assessments by component

Key parts of leg ulcer assessment may be missing.

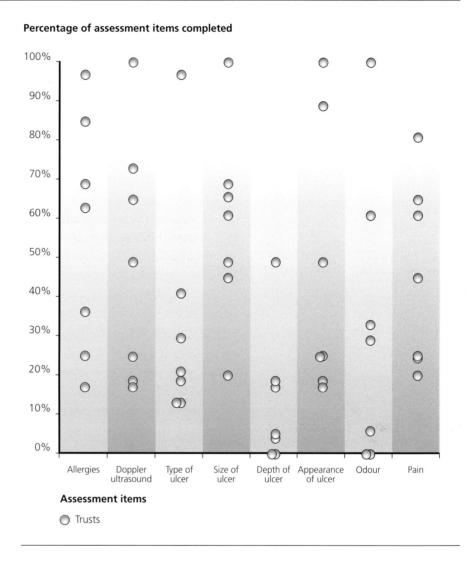

Percentage of assessment items completed

Assessment items

◯ Trusts

Source: Audit Commission reviews of assessment documentation (seven trusts)

100. In practice, district nurses often implement a conservative care plan focused on managing the problem rather than treating the underlying cause. Assessment documentation is frequently more complete than that for patients with leg ulcers. But all too often this is because the documentation is regarded as a prescription for pads. The assessment sometimes bears little relationship to the care actually provided **[CASE HISTORY D, overleaf].** However, conservative approaches to the management of incontinence are coming under increased pressure as trusts try to contain expenditure following the reintroduction of VAT on continence products delivered to patients at home. If trusts are really to contain expenditure on continence products then assessments need to be comprehensive and should lead to an appropriate evidence-based care plan.[31]

CASE HISTORY D

This woman has multiple sclerosis. *'I also have high blood pressure and suffer with incontinence, and it's rubbish. That's basically it. I don't know what else I can say because my health is going downhill and getting worse every week.'*

She was referred to the district nurse by her GP. *'She came out very quickly, filled these stupid forms in … we talked about the incontinence pads, she brought a bag full and it was "what's the best for you", and we went through. She's very kind, very understanding. When she had to do that catheter, take away the retaining fluid, she was very helpful, she didn't make me feel I was a nuisance, it was a case of, she was very aware that I was a person … I mean, because I had trouble getting on the bed and moving up, and it was difficult, we ended up having a bit of a laugh. So she made me relax and she made me feel like a human being, which a lot of people haven't done. I suppose you could say it was the rapport between me and J. She's really nice.'*

Recently she was assessed by the *'continence woman'*. *'Came out to give me the third degree, plus of course J. had to take a catheter sample of what urine I was retaining … If someone comes into your house, and it's 'come on, do that or do this', and you're made immediately to feel a stranger in your own home … I do feel that J was given a lot of forms with a lot of stupid questions to answer which was all totally unnecessary because when she* [the 'continence woman'] *came out I had to answer them all over again. So what's the point? Waste of money, waste of NHS resources … They couldn't take J's word or my word.'* She found some questions intrusive. *'Well, my sex life, and that's my business, it's nothing to do with anybody else, and that was one of the questions.'* She feels she was given poor advice. *'She said "don't take that, it will bung you up and you won't be able to wee if you take them." I went back to my neurological nurse and my neurologist and they said "rubbish". So basically she don't know what she's talking about.'*

After the visit she waited weeks for the pads and continued buying sanitary towels. *'I've phoned J and said "I still haven't got them." It took her quite a few weeks to gee them up and then a few months later they turned up because J had to make another phone call.'*

Source: Audit Commission patients' and carers' study

101. At each of the seven study site trusts assessment documentation was reviewed for a sample of between 14 and 25 new patients who had been assessed in the previous six months. Each assessment was compared against the checklist of items [BOX G] derived from guidelines on recommended practice, and a percentage completion rate was calculated.

BOX G

Components of a comprehensive continence assessment

GENERAL	SYMPTOMS	OTHER
Age	Type of incontinence	Clinical examinations and investigations
Gender	Onset of incontinence and associated factors	Frequency-volume measures
Medical history/surgical history	When incontinence occurs	Referrals to specialist nurses, medical clinicians, physiotherapists or occupational therapists
Gynaecological/obstetric history	Description of symptoms	
History of incontinence problems		
Medications	Pattern of urination and/or defaecation	
Allergies	Degree/severity of incontinence	
Mobility	Odour	
Nutritional/hydration state	Colour	
Elimination		
Skin integrity		
Understanding of health needs		
Lifestyle/social activities		

...variation in assessment quality is apparent...

Quality of assessments

102. As with leg ulcer patients, review of continence assessment documentation at the study sites showed a wide range in performance. The best trust recorded a completion rate of 70 per cent compared with only 31 per cent at the worst [EXHIBIT 19].

103. Again, when the percentage completion scores are broken down into their component parts [EXHIBIT 20] the true extent of the variation in assessment quality is apparent. For example:

- physical restrictions that impede access to the toilet may induce incontinence, either directly or in conjunction with other factors, such as diuretic therapy. Poor manual dexterity or eyesight may also affect a person's ability to remain continent. Not only is the assessment of mobility and manual dexterity important in identifying the cause of incontinence but these factors are relevant when deciding on a plan of care (Ref. 30). Most assessments recorded information on mobility but at one trust fewer than half did so;

- descriptions of urinary symptoms, such as frequency and urgency, may be confused with those of a urine infection. Individuals may try to control the frequency of urination by reducing their fluid intake and may be vulnerable to urine infections as a consequence of bladder stasis. It is recommended that any person presenting with urinary incontinence should have routine urine tests that may reveal abnormalities that indicate infection. But urine tests were recorded on only half of the assessments reviewed; and

- charting the frequency of urination and the volume of urine voided is one of the most important aids in the diagnosis and planning of care for urinary incontinence. But only one in six of the assessments reviewed included a frequency-volume chart. Performance was poor across all trusts, and at two there was no evidence of any frequency-volume charting.[32]

EXHIBIT 19

Completion scores for continence assessments by trust

The quality of continence assessment varies between trusts.

Source: Audit Commission reviews of assessment documentation

Percentage of assessment items completed

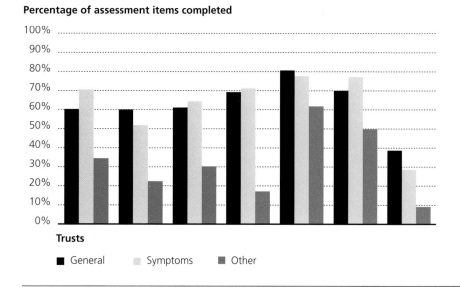

Trusts

■ General   ▨ Symptoms   ■ Other

EXHIBIT 20

Completion scores for continence assessments by component

Some continence assessments omit important information.

Percentage of assessment items completed

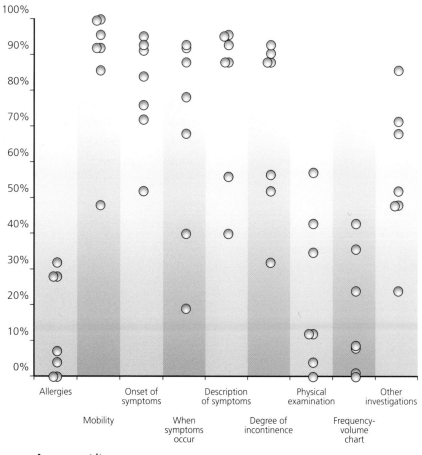

Assessment items

◯ Trusts

Source: Audit Commission reviews of assessment documentation (seven trusts)

The effects of poor assessment

104. The quality of assessment for many patients with leg ulcers or continence problems falls short of national guidelines. The consequences of an incomplete, or poor quality, assessment, can include:

- delays in care and treatment, which can leave patients feeling degraded or in pain;

- delays in referral to appropriate specialists or other agencies;

- ineffective communication between nurses, other health professionals and other agencies that may be involved in the patient's care;

- 'misdiagnosis', leading to ineffective care delivery;

- delays in 'recovery' from, or amelioration of, the problem; and

- the absence of a baseline against which to judge improvement or deterioration in the patient.

105. It is often said that poor documentation does not mean poor care, but the Audit Commission's review of assessment documentation found that some patients were receiving care from as many as five or six nurses within a short period, emphasising the need for effective communication and thorough documentation [**CASE HISTORY E**]. Equally, the perceived duplication, fragmentation and burden of some record-keeping systems need to be addressed.

CASE HISTORY E

This 58-year-old lady, who has been living alone since her husband died a year ago, has severe arthritis and a five-year history of leg ulcers. During the week she dresses the leg herself. But at the weekends a number of different district nursing staff have come in to do it. Her treatment was changed following reassessment by the district nurse, but she felt that the nurses who visited her at weekends were not properly informed.

'They don't seem to know from wherever they come from though what they're having to do, they're not told ... they don't seem to know what sort of dressings to do. I don't know why, there's a loophole somewhere between the three places. I mean all right, each time they come they put dressing changed or redone and that's it, but every week they should either take it back there and bring it back on the Monday or something, so the people on the weekends would know what to do. I think that would help.'

Source: Audit Commission patients' and carers' study

106. Limitations in the measurement of outcomes for patients with leg ulcers, and variations in clinical practice, make it virtually impossible to isolate and judge the impact of assessment quality on leg ulcer management in any systematic way. It is apparent, however, that lack of appropriate assessment may contribute to ineffective and inappropriate treatment. For example, an audit of patients at one study site showed that the type of ulcer was 'unknown' in 16 per cent of patients and these patients were being treated in a variety of ways which may or may not have been appropriate. At another study site, clinical audit revealed that 27 per cent of 'venous' leg ulcers had been present for three years or more[33] which may reflect problems with assessment, a lack of awareness about the evidence and, the unavailability of recommended treatments – such as high compression bandaging – in the community.

Improving assessment quality

107. The quality of assessment can be improved through the use of standardised, condition-specific forms which prompt the assessor to seek and record general assessment information as well as information specific to the patient's condition. Where prompts for assessment of problems like pain are absent from the documentation, more often than not nothing is recorded. Even when trusts have appropriate assessment documentation, district nurses do not always use it. Three-quarters of the district nurses responding to the Audit Commission's survey reported that their trust had separate forms for assessing patients with leg ulcers. But more than one in four of these nurses continued to use general nursing assessment forms, wound assessment forms or documentation provided by pharmaceutical company representatives.

108. Improved documentation needs to be accompanied by training.[34] In many cases, nurses completing assessment forms did not seem to know what information to record. For example, the assessment of hydration and nutrition for an elderly man with a leg ulcer failed to mention any risk factors such as mouth infections, or an inability to handle cutlery, simply commenting that he 'likes beer'.

What do patients and carers value?

109. The humanity of the district nursing service is fundamentally important to patients. Patients describe the value that they place on their relationship with the nurses. Liking and trusting someone on whom you are dependent and establishing a 'one-to-one' relationship which extends beyond the nurses' professional role are regarded as central to the quality of their care. Patients may find it difficult to voice their needs to most professionals apart from the nurses. Patients talk of feeling comfortable with district nurses, that they are able to describe their nursing needs and other anxieties that they may have. According to the patients this stems, at least in part, from the fact that their contact with the nurse is often on a frequent basis and within their own home. These are not added extras but are central to a sense of personal security and quality of life for

...there is a danger that the things that patients value most highly will be lost.

people living with illness, disability and deteriorating health. Trusts and commissioners should recognise that, with pressure on services to increase efficiency and the rise in technical, as opposed to personal, nursing care, there is a danger that some of the things that patients say they value most highly will be lost.

Perceptions of leg ulcer and continence patients

110. Patients' experiences and perceptions of care varied according to the condition for which they were receiving care:

- patients with leg ulcers had regular and frequent care compared with continence patients. Care given always involved dressing the ulcer, and the nurse's knowledge and technical skills were rated highly among this group of patients;

- patients with incontinence had varied needs depending on the cause and management of the incontinence. All these patients used incontinence pads and it was important for them that the nurse acted as an efficient liaison with the delivery services and ensured that they received adequate supplies of suitable pads; and

- for the patient with incontinence and no major causative pathology, there was often no 'care plan' and no reported discussions on how to cope with hygiene issues; assessments were patchy and did not reflect any participation by the patient. Patients with incontinence resulting from a recognised pathology were more knowledgeable and had more care relating to issues of hygiene and coping with their incontinence.

Perceptions of patients seen at home and in clinics

111. Patients' experience and perceptions of care also varied according to where they actually received it:

- all patients valued their relationship with the nurses. However, being able to establish a 'one-to-one' relationship beyond the 'professional', and liking and trusting the person who comes into your home and on whom you are dependent, was perceived by patients to be particularly important to the quality of their care. They felt that they got personal attention at home which was lacking when they visited a clinic and also felt that the nurse knew more about them and their needs. Patients may be anxious and find their condition distressing, painful and socially isolating. Having time to talk with the nurse about their condition was highly valued. The feeling of being cared for, of having the opportunity for a 'little chat', is often repeated: *'...they come and keep an eye on me and see if I'm all right, you see... I like seeing them. They tell me about their family and just that little chat, it might be five minutes, and while they're doing the dressing they sort of talk to you'*;

...some patients expressed regret when their interaction with the nurse was reduced...

- clinic patients appeared to be more focused on the nurses' skills than on personal relations. But some patients expressed regret when their interaction with the nurse was reduced; for example, if their care moved to a clinic: '*...the clinic were all right but you couldn't talk to them like you can the ones that come here... They couldn't spend a lot of time with each one of us... They used to just dress it, and '... then get on with the next one*'; and

- clinic patients expressed satisfaction with the clinic and did not express any preference for home visits. Home patients expressed satisfaction at being seen at home and had no strong objections to the idea of attending the clinic, except for negative recollections of long waiting times at hospital, and for some the problems of transport.

Carers

112. Carers had a variety of needs:

- for practical assistance. Additional personal care for the patient was sometimes provided by paid care assistants, and nurses sometimes provided teaching in basic skills when care assistants were untrained in patient management;

- for adequate supplies of incontinence pads organised by the district nurse. Supplies that are inadequate in quality or quantity, or poorly organised, cause the carer, and in some cases the patient, distress, and could become a factor in the carer being unable to cope;

- for psychological support. They value the nurses' attention to the patient whom they were looking after and also value the time that the nurse gave them to listen to their own concerns – they needed to trust her judgement and rely on her confidentiality. The feeling that resources would be available when they just could not manage any longer helps them to carry on and to feel cared for; and

- for respite care. It was highly valued when it was trusted, but changes to eligibility criteria has caused anxiety for some carers. There was also some lack of confidence in respite care due to previous poor experiences: patients had sometimes returned with reduced life skills, pressure sores or other evidence of neglect.

Getting patients' and carers' views

113. The only national measure of users' experiences of the service currently available is that relating to timed appointments for community nurses, which was introduced in the updated 1995 Patient's Charter [BOX H]. Sitting around waiting helplessly for the nurses to visit was a concern for some of the patients and carers interviewed in this study: *'Sometimes you have to stay in all day waiting for them. You don't know what time they're coming, only the day... Sometimes you find it very awkward. You want to make arrangements to do something but you can't because you don't know what time the nurse is coming...'*

114. Although the *Patient's Charter* does not specify a standard that nurses are expected to achieve in relation to agreed appointment times, the figures collected nationally recorded such consistently high levels of performance over three years that they are no longer reported.[35] But research suggests that success rates decline towards the end of the day and that G grade district nurses are less able than other grades to adhere to timed visits because they need to respond flexibly to patients' needs (Ref. 31). It is also suggested that a timeband system increases travel costs because the nurse's day is planned around agreed appointment times rather than the clustering of patients in particular areas (Ref. 31).

BOX H

Patient's Charter standards

Appointment times

'There are nurses, health visitors and midwives working in your community. From April 1995, if you need a home visit from one of these professionals, you can expect to be consulted about a convenient time. You can then expect a visit within a two-hour timeband. Exceptionally, your community nurse, health visitor or midwife may be unable to make this appointment or be delayed. In these cases, your community nurse, health visitor or midwife should let you know and make another appointment with you.'

Seeing community nurses

'You can expect to receive a visit from someone in the district nurse team or the mental health nurse:

- *within four hours (in the daytime), if you have been referred to them as an urgent patient;*

- *within two working days, if you have been referred to them as a non-urgent patient and you have not asked them to see you on any particular day; and*

- *by appointment on the day you ask for, if you give the district nursing services more than 48 hours notice.'*

Source: Ref. 32

115. Part of the new framework for assessing the performance of the NHS relates to the measurement of patient and carer experience. In order to do this, the Government is introducing an annual national survey in each health authority, which is designed to measure performance against the aspirations and expectations of users. There is a clear recognition in the White Paper that better quality and more responsive services depend on listening to, and understanding, the needs and wishes of service-users (Ref. 10). In order to apply this principle to district nursing, trusts need to complement the national survey with their own, more local and focused, processes for collecting patients' and carers' views. At the moment, they do not do it much and when they do, it is not always done well.

116. Patients and carers are often isolated, and dependent on the services that they receive. Collecting their views requires a sensitive approach [CASE HISTORY F]. Typically, service-users are asked to complete questionnaires comprising statements formulated by the service provider which may, or may not, be of importance to patients. The wording, ambiguity and superficiality of patient surveys has been criticised (Refs. 33 and 34). Sometimes patients are asked questions that they cannot be expected to answer. For example, at one study site patients were asked to rate, using a five-point scale, whether *'District nurses have the nursing/clinical skills to meet your needs'*. These surveys tended to focus on the extent to which the service achieved local or national Patient's Charter standards, rather than the perhaps less tangible 'caring' issues which patients also describe as important.

CASE HISTORY F

This 68-year-old woman is caring for her adult daughter who suffered brain damage as a baby after a whooping cough vaccination. She provides all the nursing care for her daughter, including giving her enemas. She has a disabled son and her husband has recently had triple bypass heart surgery.

A district nurse gives the daughter a B12 injection every 12 weeks. She is uncertain when the nurse will call and would very much like to know in advance. She is also uncertain about what else she can ask for, but has asked the nurses for a ramp so that she can take her daughter out in the wheelchair.

Her major need is a regular supply of the correct incontinence pads. Pads and pants are delivered every month. If there are problems, she can contact the delivery service via the nurse. She has had problems reaching the nurses, and has had to contact the delivery service herself. She wants a special pad that stays on when her daughter is walking, but has been told that it is very expensive and that she is not entitled to it. *'As you can imagine, I was very hurt. I said "my dear, I'm very grateful for this." I certainly don't take things for granted ... and I do buy a lot of stuff for her. I don't want to complain about her* [the supplies manager] *because I don't want to get the backlash from it.'*

She feels that she can ask the nurses for help: *'I know that if I am in trouble I can turn to them. I don't think I could ever be in need for anything really because, as I say, they are helpful, it's just getting hold of them now. I don't know if they are going through changes, so I'm giving them time.'*

Source: Audit Commission patients' and carers' study

...views of patients do not always coincide with those of their carers...

117. Trusts can be amateurish in their approach to obtaining feedback from patients and carers. Issues such as the timing of the survey, its reliability and validity, are seldom assessed and the method of sampling is not always reported. Surveys tend to focus on patients and ignore carers. But the needs and views of patients do not always coincide with those of their carers, and so carers' views should be assessed independently.

118. Most surveys report very high levels of patient satisfaction. Research (Refs. 34 and 35) suggests that this is a product of the measurement process as much as a reflection of patients' real opinions about services [BOX I].

119. There was little evidence at study sites that the views of patients gathered in these ways led to significant changes in service delivery. If surveys have a role, it is probably in exposing the most conspicuous elements of dissatisfaction [BOX J].

120. One study site trust, working with the local community health council, has undertaken a pilot project using in-depth semi-structured interviews with patients and carers to get a more balanced picture of patients' perceptions. Interviews were based on issues that were identified as important by patients themselves, as well as areas that managers and clinicians wanted to consider. The exercise yielded considerably more useful data than the traditional approach, and the trust planned to establish a panel of users who would be consulted on a regular basis.

121. If trusts are to have a clearer understanding about service priorities and standards from patients' and carers' viewpoints, they need to communicate clear and specific objectives to users and to adopt processes that enable users' perspectives to be heard regularly and sensitively.

BOX I

Problems with patient satisfaction surveys

There are several reasons why patient satisfaction surveys may give a falsely reassuring picture:

- patients may be reluctant to criticise services on which they are dependent;

- patient responses may be influenced by their perception of their illness or their circumstances – for example, feeling grateful for any treatment that they have waited a long time for;

- patients may have few, if any, expectations on which to base an evaluation of the care that they receive;

- in general, older patients tend to report being more satisfied than younger patients, irrespective of the input that they actually receive;

- the survey tools may not be sensitive enough to elicit respondents' precise views; and

- non-respondents may be less satisfied than the respondents.

BOX J

A survey of users' views of the service

One study site trust had recently used a postal questionnaire comprising 12 closed and 3 open-ended questions to obtain users' views of its district nursing service. A sample of just over 500 users was selected from those who had been discharged from the service in the previous year and who had been on the caseload for six months or longer. This sample has the advantage of avoiding current (dependent) users, but means excluding the views of short- and long-term users. The survey relied on the ability of former patients to recall events accurately and excluded patients from ethnic minorities, patients who were blind and patients who could not read or write. It had a 45 per cent response rate.

This survey covered:

- visiting patterns
- duration of contact
- service accessibility
- information provision

- educative role of the nurse
- continuity of care
- location of care
- meeting needs

It is difficult to know what the trust would do with some of the findings. For example, 10 per cent of respondents thought that their needs were not met by the district nursing service. But the survey did not collect information on what needs remained unmet and whether these were needs that the district nursing service should be meeting. Like many such surveys, the questions elicit responses that could not provide sufficient information to drive operational change.

Source: Audit Commission study site

Improving the quality of care

122. Improving the quality of clinical care, in line with the principles of clinical governance introduced in *The new NHS – Modern and Dependable* (Ref. 10), requires trusts to take a comprehensive approach. Changing clinical practice is a complex business and many different approaches have been adopted. Senior managers repeatedly express their desire to encourage a self-evaluative and responsive culture among district nurses that will allow clinical practice to evolve and reflect emerging evidence of effectiveness. Organisational culture and managers' attitudes are just as important in leading and effecting change as legislative directives.

123. If they are to improve the quality of care that they provide, trusts have to address several key areas. These include:

- developing clinical supervision;
- using clinical audit and clinical effectiveness; and
- making the best use of specialist nurses.

...district nurses' clinical work...is rarely overseen...

Developing clinical supervision

124. District nursing is largely a solitary occupation – one nurse, one patient. Finding out how well you are doing, and how you could do better, can be difficult without well-designed and managed systems for audit, feedback and education. Furthermore, district nurses' clinical work – mainly undertaken in the patient's home – is rarely overseen by peers or managers. This makes the quality of clinical care difficult to monitor [BOX K].

125. One of the ways in which trusts might seek to promote clinical effectiveness and to form a self-evaluative and responsive culture is through the process of clinical supervision. Clinical supervision *'...brings practitioners and skilled supervisors together to reflect on practice. Supervision aims to identify solutions to problems, improve practice and increase understanding of professional issues'* (Ref. 36).[36]

126. The potential benefits of clinical supervision have been highlighted for more than ten years. But community trusts have – for a variety of reasons – been slower to implement it among their district nursing staff than among other nurses. The Audit Commission's survey of district nurses found that fewer than half (46 per cent) had received clinical supervision in the last 12 months.[37] And, where district nurses had received supervision, half had done so quarterly or less frequently and many for only an hour. But at trusts with protected time for clinical supervision, almost three-quarters of nurses reported having taken part in clinical supervision over the previous 12 months (compared with two-fifths in trusts without protected time) and their most recent clinical supervision was twice as long (on average three hours).

BOX K

Venous leg ulcers – frequency of treatment

The national clinical guidelines on the management of venous leg ulcers recommend the use of high-compression systems that are capable of sustaining compression *'for at least a week'* (Ref. 28). It is generally accepted that, for optimum wound healing, the dressing should be changed as little as possible. But a recent clinical audit at one study site revealed that almost half the patients were having their dressings changed more than once a week, including 7 per cent who were having daily dressing changes. The problem is compounded by the fact that, in this trust, nurse managers made almost no attempt to observe the clinical practice of district nurses and there were no other supervision structures in place. Since nursing staff costs are the major component of expenditure on leg ulcer treatment and one determinant of this expenditure is the frequency of visits, this finding is clearly an issue for both clinical, and cost, effectiveness.

127. None of the study site trusts had an established system of supervision, although several were piloting schemes in particular localities or for specific grades.[38] The schemes for clinical supervision introduced by study sites vary widely in their key features (Table 1). For example, the recommended frequency of sessions varied from monthly to quarterly, while the ratio of supervisors to supervised ranged from 1:1 to 1:8.

TABLE 1

Key features of clinical supervision for district nurses

Trusts:	A	B	C	D	E
Date introduced	Pilot October 1997 to April 1998	Not known	October – December 1997	February 1996	February 1997
Style	One-to-one (for G&H grades); group supervision for others	One-to-one	One-to-one (for G&H grades); group supervision for others	One-to-one	One-to-one
Supervisors	Community nurses in same locality	Clinical team leaders for G&H grades; G&H grades for other staff	23 G&H grade district nurses	18 G&H grade district nurses	Not identified
Supervisor training	?	?	2 days	3 days	None arranged
Ratio of supervisors to supervised	1:1 in pilot	Not stated	Maximum 1:6	Planned 1:8	Not known
Grades	All registered; but starting with G&H	All grades	All 'clinical' staff starting with G&H	Registered nurses	All community nurses
Participation	Voluntary	Not stated	Compulsory	Not stated	None
Frequency	Every 1-2 months	Negotiable	Every 2-3 months	Monthly	Monthly
Duration	1-1.5 hours	Negotiable	1 hour	1 hour	1 hour

Source: Audit Commission study sites

128. Managers at trusts were clear that clinical supervision must not be threatening or judgemental, that it must not be a substitute for counselling (when appropriate), or for education and training. But practitioners were more wary. The term 'supervision' clearly had negative connotations for some district nurses – implying a monitoring process where a supervisor will tell the supervisee what to do and how to do it. Others were concerned that if the content was documented it could be used for other purposes – for example, disciplining the nurse. One trust had endeavoured to sidestep this concern by referring instead to 'clinical support'. The Audit Commission's survey of district nurses found that those who have taken part in clinical supervision are more positively disposed towards it **[EXHIBIT 21]**.

129. District nursing has been slow to embrace clinical supervision. Few study site trusts have managed to establish it as an integral part of a high-quality service and none has evaluated it. Most trusts have developed guidelines for clinical supervision, designed documentation so that participants can record the content of clinical supervision sessions, and have trained clinical supervisors. But comparatively few district nurses are actually receiving supervision on a regular basis.[39]

EXHIBIT 21

Proportion of district nurses who agree with statements about clinical supervision
District nurses who have taken part in clinical supervision are more positively disposed towards it.

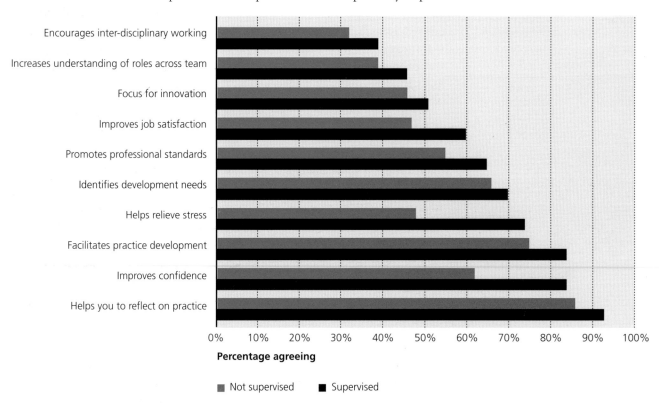

Source: Audit Commission survey of district nurses

3 • IMPROVING THE QUALITY OF CARE

...a non-challenging professional culture... can lead to a state of inertia that prevents best practice from being passed on.

130. Recent research concluded that district nursing exhibited '*a non-challenging professional culture that could sometimes stand in the way of optimal patient care. This has important implications for clinical effectiveness, as a non-challenging culture can lead to a state of inertia that prevents best practice from being passed on; it can also lead to variations in practice and inequities in service provision*' (Ref. 37). Discussions about care for specific patients tend to be at an interpersonal level between nurses. Without a more formal mechanism for clinical peer review, variations in practice will remain and some patients will not receive the most up-to-date and clinically effective care. Learning how to review critically and how to support colleagues effectively may be more important than learning how to review research; it is also likely to be far more difficult to implement.

Clinical effectiveness and clinical audit

131. Trusts should have robust methods of measuring standards of clinical quality (in terms of care processes and health outcomes). Clinical audit is a key quality improvement process which enables practitioners to examine their practices against standards based on evidence of good practice from research or consensus. But since there are few evidence-based good practice standards in district nursing, it is perhaps not surprising to find clinical audit in this area under-developed. At most study sites, district nurses saw clinical audit as a marginal activity, something done to them rather than by them. In most trusts, district nurses had little or no opportunity to influence the choice of audit topics and audit activity was not part of their day-to-day activity. Even where audits covered topics that concerned district nurses, few trusts had an established cycle of audit and follow-up that could demonstrate the impact of any changes that had been implemented.

132. There are comparatively few outcome measures that can be used to gauge the standards of care for most of the conditions with which district nurses deal. But even where outcome measures do exist, they are not always used. For example, there are a number of different ways of measuring outcomes for patients with leg ulcers.[40] But in practice, the majority of trusts use only the crude healing rate to measure the performance of their service. On its own, this may give quite a false view of the service. The recurrence rate[41] is a proxy for equally important aspects of leg ulcer care and can be used as a measure for the success of patient education, follow-up (for Doppler reassessment and re-measurement for compression hosiery) and advice about diet and exercise.[42]

133. Equally, a number of different outcome measures can be used to assess the management of incontinence. For example: the restoration of bladder or bowel control; the improvement in one or more symptoms; improvements in self-image and self-esteem; improvements in health (such as a reduction in skin excoriation). In practice, however, most trusts do not evaluate the effectiveness of their services against such measures.

134. If they are to improve how they care for patients, district nurses need to know where they are least effective and how they can improve. There is much that trusts can do to help staff to improve their effectiveness [CASE STUDY 5].

135. District nurses cannot always access libraries and research-based literature easily. For example, almost half the district nurses responding to the Audit Commission's survey did not know whether they had access to the Cochrane Database of Systematic Reviews. Information and clinical effectiveness strategies need to take account of any such limits to access [BOX L].

CASE STUDY 5

A clinical effectiveness strategy

Severn NHS Trust has developed a clinical effectiveness strategy which includes:

- ensuring access and dissemination of information on clinical effectiveness, audit and guidelines to staff, including provision of branch libraries in localities;

- establishing a baseline of existing staff skills in relation to clinical effectiveness;

- establishing fora in which clinical effectiveness issues can be addressed;

- providing opportunities for staff to learn how to access databases effectively, to perform literature searches and to learn critical appraisal skills;

- forming a dissemination strategy that enables widespread access to relevant literature and access to electronic databases of authoritative and peer-reviewed evidence;

- supporting staff in fulfilling clinical and professional development required by regulatory bodies;

- exploring and researching methods to facilitate access for the public to evidence-based information; and

- participating in comparative exercises: benchmarking, outcome measures and national audits.

Source: Audit Commission study site

BOX L

The Primary Care Partnership

In 1996 Northumberland Community Health NHS Trust and Northumberland Health Authority formed the Primary Care Partnership, a joint approach to the development of primary health care teams through a co-ordinating centre. Historically, development was dependent on the teams themselves, with some input from the trust and health authority. But there was:

- a lack of easily available information;

- no co-ordination of good practice;

- poor communication across the county;

- a lack of shared expertise;

- no identification of the development needs of primary health care teams;

- no continuing support for initiatives;

- no quality markers.

Through the pooled resources of both organisations, a single co-ordinating centre has been established where primary health care teams can access:

- advice on all aspects of primary health care, accessible by telephone/fax and email;

- a database on audits, research and primary care developments which is accessible in a format to suit the user and;

- a diagnostic self-assessment tool for the identification of primary care development needs.

The Primary Care Partnership is a virtual organisation with joint membership, salaries and resources provided by the health authority, community trust and primary health care teams. The workforce includes a range of project teams from across the organisation as well as established clinical teams including district nurses in the posts of primary care development nurses.

Source: Audit Commission study site

136. Community nurses are mostly influenced by practice-based, or experiential, knowledge. Success, in terms of changing practice, depends on presenting research-based information in a form that has meaning for practitioners (Ref. 38). In many of the trusts visited, clinical nurse specialists had developed clinical practice guidelines, but in some there was little evidence that implementation strategies were being developed alongside the guidelines. Guidelines that are not reinforced by a practical implementation stratgey are unlikely to be adopted or to result in change (Ref. 39).

Making best use of specialist nurses

137. As clinical leaders, specialist nurses have several roles to play in improving the quality of care given by district nurses. These roles include:

- providing professional advice, support and information to practitioners[43] (and to patients);
- involving practitioners in developing guidelines on clinical practice;
- providing education and training to update staff;
- monitoring assessment;
- monitoring standards via clinical audit; and
- clinical management for some patients (for example, via assessment and diagnostic tests) [CASE HISTORY G].

CASE HISTORY G

This woman patient has multiple health problems including a five-year history of incontinence. She was buying babies' nappies and incontinence pads because sanitary towels were no longer sufficient. She had frequent contact with doctors but her continence problems had not been picked up. She had mentioned them to the practice nurse: *'When I spoke to the nurse in the surgery she gave me a sheet, (of exercise instructions) but a sheet doesn't really tell you how to do it.'*

About six months ago, a new GP referred her to the continence nurse specialist at the clinic. The continence nurse went *'...through all the exercises, and checks that you're doing them right. She gives you the confidence to do it, you know what I mean? She has been absolutely brilliant yes, I must admit... I've been doing all these pelvic exercises all the rest of it, ... I just wish I'd done something about it years ago.'* She has also been issued with the appropriate incontinence pads which has made her more comfortable and confident.

She values the relationship with the nurse and is optimistic that she will soon be able to go without pads at all. *'She made it all matter of fact, and it was very easy and as I say quite pleasant and I'm quite happy to go ... There was no stigma which I thought I might feel ... everybody would know what I'd gone for, but it was all very discreet and I felt quite comfortable with it. "If you're prepared to put the effort in", that's what she said to me, "you put the effort in for me, I'll put the effort in for you". As I say, I can't say that it hasn't been fairer than that because it certainly seems to have worked this way. So no, as far as she's concerned I'm one hundred per cent really pleased with her, she has been brilliant."*

Source: Audit Commission patients' and carers' study

138. But the number of clinical nurse specialists is often small relative to the number of community nursing staff [EXHIBIT 22].[44] Not only do many have to relate to a large number of district nurses, but they often have other responsibilities such as managing their own caseload[45] and the administration of equipment and supplies. In many cases, specialist nurses argue that they are used inappropriately; for example, to monitor and manage the supply of continence products or pressure-relieving mattresses. At one study site, where part-time clerical support had been withdrawn from the tissue viability nurses, supplies management had become the most time-consuming part of their job and was reported to have delayed the development of a new assessment form and clinical guidelines.

139. The Audit Commission's survey of district nurses found that a higher proportion of those with access to clinical nurse specialists have condition-specific assessment documentation, recent training in assessment and guidelines on clinical practice.

EXHIBIT 22

WTE district nurses per clinical nurse specialist

The number of specialist nurses is often small relative to the number of district nursing staff.

WTE district nursing staff per clinical nurse specialist

Trusts

Source: Audit Commission survey of trusts

...setting may be less important than ensuring correct assessment and management.

140. Clinics run by specialist nurses are widely regarded as offering the opportunity to form centres of excellence – for example, in the management of leg ulcers – and to achieve improved patient outcomes [CASE STUDY 6]. But setting may be less important than ensuring correct assessment and management. The available trials do not provide sufficient information to discriminate between the effects of setting, nurse training, the role of the specialist nurse, the use of compression bandaging, or protocols for treatment and referral. Nevertheless, most of the study site trusts had developed, or were establishing, community leg ulcer clinics.

141. Problems with the unavailability of evidence-based treatments – for example, high-compression leg ulcer bandaging systems – have also caused difficulty for the implementation of clinically effective care in the community. District nurses have always been reliant on obtaining treatments on prescription, and many items, such as four-layer bandaging systems, are available only in secondary care or to those trusts and fundholders which chose to purchase these items for patients at home. The introduction of PCGs with unified budgets covering most aspects of care could remove some of these barriers.

CASE STUDY 6

Community leg ulcer clinics

In a cross-trust review of the management of leg ulcer patients, Wigan and Bolton Health Authority compared patients who received care from the generic district nursing team with those receiving care from nurse-led community leg ulcer clinics. The traditional approach was found to be less effective, with poorer healing rates and higher costs[46]. Among the characteristics that the report cites are:

- lack of a co-ordinated approach to leg ulcer management;
- lack of awareness of research evidence;
- low levels of referral for specialist opinion;
- inadequate assessment, leading to misdiagnosis and inappropriate treatment; and
- lack of training and education.

The establishment of community leg ulcer clinics run by a team of district nurses with special expertise in leg ulcer management and supported by appropriate medical input was considered to be the most effective way of addressing these issues, improving healing rates and making more effective use of district nursing time.

Source: Audit Commission study site

142. Most specialist nurses rely on networks of 'link' nurses to disseminate information, good practice and ideas to other community nursing staff. These are district nursing staff with an interest, and sometimes additional education and training,[47] in a particular clinical area. But the numbers[48] of link nurses, and the ways in which they perform their role, differ substantially between trusts. In some cases, the role is largely passive – for example, simply maintaining a boxfile of information for others to use – while in others, the role is more extended and may include undertaking assessments and running clinics, as well as providing advice, training and cascading information from the clinical nurse specialist [CASE STUDY 7].

143. There are two main problems with the link nurse role:

- in most trusts, the link nurse role is additional to the nurses' current workload, so the amount of time that each link nurse puts into the role is variable; and

- in some trusts, community staff nurses are used as link nurses. They can find it difficult to advise qualified district nurses (who may be their line managers) about aspects of their clinical practice.

144. As a consequence, the dissemination of information, good practice and innovation from specialist nurses to district nurses can be patchy. Few trusts have anything more than anecdotal evidence that the processes for dissemination actually work. Systematic means of monitoring whether lessons for clinical practice have been learnt are rare.

CASE STUDY 7

Continence link nurse system

In 1997 Northumberland Community Health NHS Trust recruited five district nurses (trained in continence promotion and incontinence management) to support the work of the continence nurse specialist. Each nurse has an agreed number of hours (sometimes referred to as 'protected hours') in which to fulfil the function. A referral pathway was developed for accessing the continence advisory service:

- initial assessments to be conducted by the appropriate community nurse;

- referral to the link nurse for advice when planned management has failed; poor compliance; catheter management problems; discussion before referring on to the continence adviser; and

- patients with complex or multiple problems who require investigation procedures will be referred to the continence adviser.

Improved clinical practice results from using link nurses to:

- act as a local resource to district nurses, providing advice and cascading information about good practice;

- provide in-service training for district nursing staff; and

- assist in assessing patients and thereby provide direct examples of good practice in completing continence assessments and implementing management plans.

Source: Audit Commission study site

...district nurses need to know where they are least effective...

Next steps

145. If they are to improve how they care for patients, district nurses need to know where they are least effective and how they can improve. To help them to do this, trusts need to make simultaneous progress on each of the three priority areas identified here. Senior managers need to be genuinely involved in, and committed to, each of these areas and the methods for improving practice need to be reviewed critically to see if they are achieving their desired impact:

- trusts need to address the apparent indifference to clinical supervision by emphasising its positive role in promoting the best standards of care and by sanctioning time for it to occur. What is important is that supervision occurs, that the arrangements are clear, that it is done by somebody who has sufficient authority to tackle flaws in clinical practice and to act upon any training needs that are identified. This will help trusts to ensure that problems with clinical performance are recognised at an early stage and dealt with promptly;

- clinical audit should not be regarded as optional. It needs to be embedded as commonplace, with district nurses routinely involved in the selection, design, implementation and reporting of clinical audit projects. Trusts need to ensure that clinical audit is effective in securing worthwhile and lasting improvements in quality of care through training and skills development, and by monitoring and reporting clinical audit activities; and

- trusts need to ensure that evidence-based practice is in day-to-day use. Clinical nurse specialists can play a key role in supporting this by developing standards and guidelines, providing clinical leadership and ensuring that good practice is systematically disseminated. But they need the appropriate infrastructure and support to do so.

NATIONAL REPORT • FIRST ASSESSMENT

RECOMMENDATIONS

3   Improving the Quality of Care

The quality of patient assessment could be improved if trusts:

1   reviewed and, where necessary, revised assessment documentation, to ensure that it includes prompts for assessment in key areas and uses standard assessment tools where appropriate

2   used peer review to monitor the quality of assessment and audited the outcomes of district nursing interventions, on a regular basis

Services would reflect users' views better if trusts:

3   improved the methods and frequency with which they collect information about patients'and carers' experiences

4   used information about users' experiences when taking decisions about changes to services

Clinical effectiveness would be increased if trusts:

5   reviewed the role and activity of clinical nurse specialists to ensure that expensive clinical nurse specialist time is not spent inappropriately and that link nurses have the time, support and training needed for them to perform an effective role

6   developed and implemented evidence-based clinical guidelines and protocols

7   encourage the use and local ownership of clinical audit to measure clinical practice against agreed standards

8   make sure that practice-based staff have access to systematic reviews of effectiveness and devise an implementation strategy for clinical guidelines

9   create and promote networks for effective clinical peer review and support

4

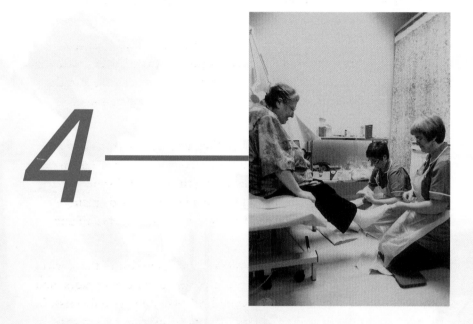

Improving Service Efficiency

Service costs differ considerably due largely to variations in
staffing levels and grade-mix. How district nurses spend their
time also varies widely, but more clinical and administrative
work could be delegated, freeing up district nurses' time to
provide more clinical leadership and team management. In
many trusts, efficiency and effectiveness could also be
improved by providing more services in clinics, where
appropriate, and by reviewing the need for,
and organisation of, out-of-hours care.

Introduction

146. Nationally, district nursing services cost an estimated £650 million.[49] Between 75 and 80 per cent of this expenditure goes on staff salaries [EXHIBIT 23]. But there are considerable variations between trusts in the staffing resource dedicated to district nursing when compared with the population served. For example, there is a 43 per cent difference in staff expenditure per head of population over 75 between trusts in the top and bottom quartiles. This chapter examines the reasons why these differences arise.

147. In part, the differences in expenditure simply reflect the fact that staffing levels vary significantly between trusts. In general, trusts have not taken a strategic overview of the total numbers of staff that they need in relation to the population that they serve and any substitute and complementary services available.

148. But, in addition to differences in staffing levels, some trusts pay more per wte than others because they employ proportionally fewer nursing auxiliaries or have a richer grade-mix among the registered staff. Decisions about changing the mix of staff tend to take place on an incremental basis, as individuals leave teams, without reference to any overall strategy.

149. Grade-mix is clearly important in determining the cost of the service. Additionally, the way in which the trust uses staff in different grades, and at different times, will also impact on both efficiency and effectiveness. In some trusts, district nurses spend far more time delivering patient care than in others. As a consequence, they may spend comparatively little time on clinical and team management. Similarly, trusts vary in the extent to which they use clinics as a means of improving service efficiency. Trust managers are often unable to make more efficient use of staff time because they do not have access to appropriate management information.

150. Even where a trust gets all these components right, its ability to deliver quality services to patients effectively and efficiently may be affected by the extent to which it relies on temporary staff to provide cover for shortages of, and absences among, district nursing staff.

EXHIBIT 23

The costs of a typical district nursing service

Three-quarters of trust expenditure is on staff salaries.

Salaries **£3.26m**

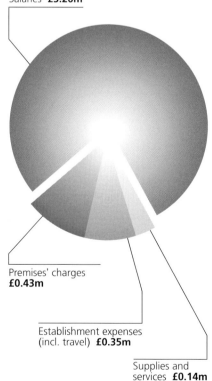

Premises' charges
£0.43m

Establishment expenses
(incl. travel) **£0.35m**

Supplies and
services **£0.14m**

Source: Audit Commission study site

Number and mix of staff employed

151. The number of district nursing staff per 1,000 population over 75 varies by 43 per cent between the top and bottom quartiles [EXHIBIT 24]. This variation might reflect differences in the health needs of populations, but it could also reflect differences in service efficiency.

152. In addition to differences in staffing levels, there is variation in staff costs per wte, with a 6 per cent difference between the top and bottom quartiles and a 30 per cent difference between trusts at the extremes. These differences reflect the fact that some trusts employ proportionally fewer nursing auxiliaries – averaging 18 per cent (but varying from 5 per cent to 37 per cent) – or have a richer grade-mix among their registered staff.

153. There are no national data on grade-mix changes, but evidence from study sites [EXHIBIT 25] suggests a substantial drop in the proportion of qualified district nurses since the early 1990s. Nationally, the Audit Commission's survey of trusts shows that the proportion of staff at G and H grades fell in two-thirds of trusts between 1995 and 1997.[50] Overall, they have declined from 38 per cent to 35 per cent of the total staffing, while the proportion in D, E and F grade posts has risen from 41 to 45 per cent.

EXHIBIT 24

WTE district nursing staff per 1,000 population over 75

The resources put into district nursing vary widely.

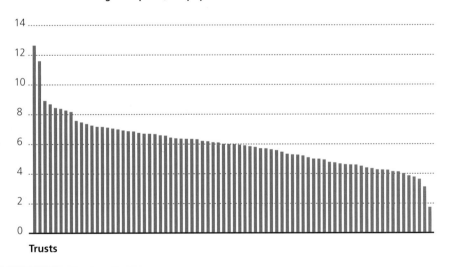

WTE district nursing staff per 1,000 population over 75

Source: Audit Commission survey of trusts

EXHIBIT 25

Grade-mix in district nursing, 1992/93 and 1997/98

The proportion of qualified district nurses has dropped.

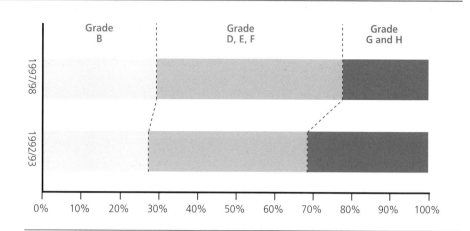

Source: Audit Commission study site

154. Despite these changes, the proportion of staff who are qualified district nurses varies between trusts from fewer than one-fifth to more than half [**EXHIBIT 26**] and it can also differ significantly between areas within a trust. These differences are not explained in terms of patient needs.

EXHIBIT 26

Grade-mix in district nursing by trust

Qualified district nurses account for fewer than one-fifth, to more than half, of all staff.

Percentage of district nursing staff

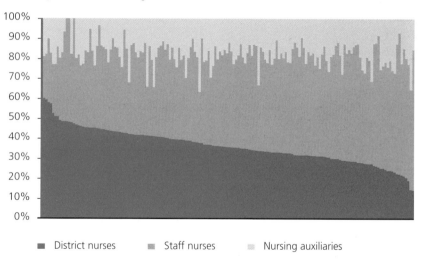

■ District nurses   ■ Staff nurses   ▪ Nursing auxiliaries

Source: Audit Commission survey of trusts

Staff deployment

155. Qualified district nurses are the most expensive element in staff costs. How they spend their time varies widely and in some trusts this valuable resource is not used to best effect, thus undermining the efficiency of the whole team. There are opportunities for district nurses to delegate more clinical work to staff nurses – safely and with proper guidelines and training – and to make better use of nursing auxiliaries. Freeing up district nurses' time to provide more clinical leadership for, and management of, the team is directly linked to improving the quality of care that patients receive.

Patient and non-patient time

156. Overall, patient-related activity (including travel[51]) accounts for more than three-quarters of staff time. About half of this time is spent in direct contact with patients or carers. This figure is consistent across trusts (ranging from 51 to 54 per cent), despite the fact that they vary in their approaches to care delivery (for example, in the amount of clinic work) and in travelling time. On average, a further 12 per cent of time is spent on patient management (including administrative work related to a specific patient, case conferences, caseload management and review) and 14 to 18 per cent on travel.

157. The proportions of time that nurses spend with patients and in non-patient related activity varies by grade. On average, nursing auxiliaries and healthcare assistants spend the largest proportion of time (60 per cent) in direct patient care, while qualified district nurses undertake most patient management and most non-patient-related activity (other administration, teaching and learning). Staff nurses spend 8 per cent more time on patient care than district nurses but only 4 per cent less time on patient management – including liaison with other agencies and caseload management [EXHIBIT 27].

158. Qualified district nurses are comparatively expensive and it is important that their particular skills are used appropriately. In a 37.5 hour working week, the average qualified district nurse spends about 14 hours in contact with patients and 5.5 hours on patient management.[52] Even when travel is excluded, there are significant variations in the proportion of time that qualified district nurses spend on patient and non-patient-related activity. Some qualified district nurses spend most of their time on direct patient care, leaving little time for patient and team management [EXHIBIT 28].

159. On average, qualified district nurses spent just over 20 per cent of their time (excluding travel) on patient management, but this ranges from 11 per cent to 25 per cent at the top and bottom quartiles. This difference appears to be unrelated to the time that they spend in direct patient care. It is clear that some district nurses spend very little time on the activities – such as liaising with other agencies and managing caseloads – which would do most to improve service efficiency and patient care.

EXHIBIT 27

Distribution of district nursing time by activity category and type of nurse

On average, qualified district nurses spend less than half their time in direct patient contact.

Percentage of time

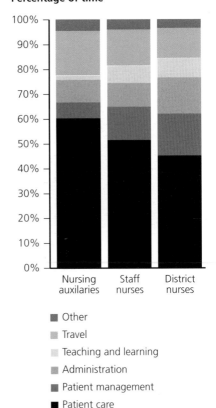

- Other
- Travel
- Teaching and learning
- Administration
- Patient management
- Patient care

Source: Audit Commission diary exercises

EXHIBIT 28

Percentage of time spent by district nursing sisters on direct patient contact

Some qualified district nurses spend most of their time on direct patient care, leaving little time for patient and team management.

Source: Audit Commission diary exercises

Percentage of time spent on direct patient care

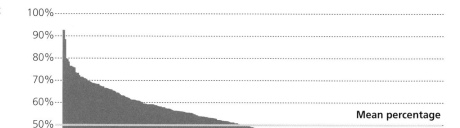

District nurses

---

160. One in six district nurses spent more than one-quarter of their time on non-patient-related administration[53] [EXHIBIT 29], activities that do not require their professional input. But few trusts have quantified the amount of time spent on such duties.

EXHIBIT 29

Percentage of time spent by district nurses on administration

Some qualified district nurses spent more than one-quarter of their time on non-patient-related administration.

Source: Audit Commission diary exercises

Percentage of time spent on administration

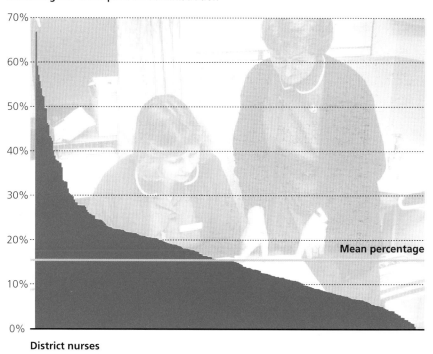

District nurses

Some trusts are expanding the role of staff nurses to encompass first assessments...

161. If district nurses are going to have more time for patient management then they need to reduce the amount of time that they spend on non-patient-related administration and entrust some of their clinical work to others. Some trusts are beginning to address this issue by expanding the role of staff nurses to encompass first assessments for selected patient groups [CASE STUDY 8]. But district nurses remain the caseload-holders and as such have continuing responsibility for the care of all patients on the caseload. While some tasks can be delegated some of the time, the decision should remain with the district nurse, in consultation with the team, so that the most appropriately skilled person carries out a particular visit or task in relation to the patient's current needs.

CASE STUDY 8

Delegating patient assessment

There is no evidence to support the view that qualified district nurses need always undertake first assessments, yet in many trusts this is the formal position. Indeed, assessment and care planning is frequently written into the job descriptions of district nurses and explicitly excluded from those of community staff nurses. In practice, community staff nurses do undertake initial assessments. But practice is inconsistent, and delegation occurs without guidelines and without additional training.

When staff nurses have made the first assessment, district nurses usually make a follow-up visit within 24 hours.[54] But follow-up visits seldom lead to changes in the assessment or care plan, other than where the patient's needs have altered, and these could equally have been identified by the staff nurse.

Southampton NHS Community Trust set up a pilot study in 1994 to evaluate the appropriateness of delegating first visits and initial assessments to community staff nurses. First visits are delegated by the district nurse on the basis of expected patient needs (derived from standardised referral documentation which was introduced at the same time). Patients suitable for delegated first visits are classified into one of two groups, short-term and longer-term (more than five visits but with discharge within a few weeks). Assessments for patients requiring terminal care and those needing complex or long-term care packages (for example, multiple sclerosis, motor neurone disease) are not delegated. Staff nurses can call the district nurse using a pager if they discover that a delegated patient has more complex needs or is likely to require long-term care. Assessments completed by the community staff nurse are discussed with, and countersigned by, the district nurse who retains continuing responsibility as caseholder.

cont./

CASE STUDY 8 (cont.)

Evaluation found that the job satisfaction of both staff nurses and district nurses increased as a result of delegation and that district nurses had more time available for other activities. Continuity of care also improved and there were no adverse comments from patients or GPs.

Staff nurses in all teams now take on this expanded role once they have worked in the community for 12 to 18 months. Just under one-third of first visits are delegated to community staff nurses; fewer than one in ten are referred back to the district nurse. Assessments can be undertaken more quickly and are more likely to be done by the nurse who will provide the care.

As a consequence of delegating first visits, district nurses have more time to spend with those patients who require complex packages of care and to undertake other aspects of their management role (for example, developing protocols and standards, and undertaking staff appraisal and clinical supervision). In turn, some nursing activities – simple dressings, eye drops and enemas – have been delegated from staff nurses to nursing auxiliaries.

Source: Audit Commission trust visit

162. In some trusts, and in some teams, there may be further scope for nursing auxiliaries to undertake a larger share of the more routine nursing tasks which are currently being undertaken by registered nurses.[55] In one trust, for example, money from the district nursing budget has been used to buy phlebotomy time and to retrain two nursing auxiliaries as phlebotomists. At another trust, an extended nursing auxiliary role was introduced in 1997 which included use of nebulisers, taking venous blood, naso-pharyngeal suction, gastrostomy feeding, insertion of medicated suppositories, application of simple dressings, taking and recording of blood pressure, assisting with terminal care and blood glucose monitoring.

Using temporary staff

...the use and costs of agency and bank nurses have risen...

163. In many trusts, the use and costs of agency and bank nurses have risen in recent years. At one study site trust, expenditure on bank staff for district nursing rose by 45 per cent between 1995/96 and 1996/97 and by 13 per cent in 1997/98. Across the seven study sites, 6 per cent of hours worked were provided by bank staff. But in one trust, 18 per cent of hours worked, and 20 per cent of patient-care hours, were provided by bank nurses. Costs are greatest where sickness absence is high, where there is more long-term use of temporary staff to cover vacant posts and where rigid practice attachment has precluded informal cover arrangements between teams. At study sites, the amount of time lost through sickness absence ranged from 5 to 7 per cent of nurses' contracted hours. At one study site, the salary and on-costs of sickness absence were estimated to be in excess of £125,000, without accounting for bank staff costs. Yet there was no evidence that the trust had a strategy for managing attendance.

164. Levels of bank staff use are often related more to their availability than to demand for them. In one study site, almost one-quarter of the requests for bank staff were unfilled in 1997/98. The position was poorest for staff nurses, whom the trust found difficult to recruit and retain in the face of growing competition from two neighbouring acute hospital trusts.[56] At another site, one in ten requests for bank staff were either unfilled or only partially satisfied, either because a bank nurse with the skills requested was not available or because a bank nurse was not available to cover the full shift. Difficulties such as these will clearly affect the quality and availability of the service to patients.

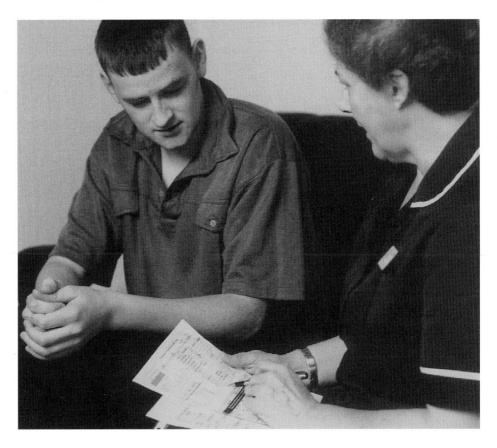

...there are widespread inconsistencies in the extent to which training is provided...

165. High levels of bank or agency staff usage raise questions about the continuity and quality of care being delivered. Although some bank staff regularly work with the same district nursing team, or group of teams, others may be more peripatetic and unfamiliar with the regular patients and local protocols and standards. Although the UKCC requires individual nurses to be responsible for ensuring that they are professionally up to date, there are widespread inconsistencies in the extent to which training is provided to bank staff (for example, in the use of local assessment documentation). In some trusts, bank staff receive induction training only in health and safety issues such as moving and handling.

166. On average, bank staff spend about 54 per cent of their time in direct patient contact and a further 8 per cent on patient management. But, in some trusts, the patient contact time can be fewer than 40 per cent of worked hours. Some bank nurses spend less than 20 per cent of their time on patient care or patient management while others spend up to 15 per cent of their time on non-patient-related administration. Trusts need to be sure that bank staff are being used appropriately.

167. But many trusts do not have sufficiently reliable or comprehensive information to promote the efficient management of bank staff:

- there is no regular monitoring of bank usage or monitoring of unfilled requests;
- there are seldom records of why bank staff are requested;
- there is little monitoring of individual's availability against requests; and
- there may be no information on bank shifts organised locally.

168. The arrangements for organising bank cover vary considerably. There are four broad, and sometimes overlapping, systems:

- cover is arranged on an informal basis between neighbouring district nursing teams;
- district nursing teams keep their own list and arrange cover by telephoning individuals who might be available to work. This can be time-consuming, especially at holiday times when fewer bank staff may be available;
- bank staff are recruited, and requests handled, at a locality level. This can result in higher administration costs than with a centralised system, as well as in inconsistencies in, for example, the induction and training of bank staff; and
- bank staff are organised centrally. In these trusts, recruitment, induction, training and deployment are administered by one or more bank co-ordinators.[57] Bank co-ordinators can save district nurses time, although bank cover sometimes has to be arranged at short notice, at the weekend or outside office hours, and may still be done by district nurses.

169. Where it is informed by a constantly updated and appropriately structured database,[58] the centrally co-ordinated model works best. Where central co-ordination is combined with delegated budgets, it can lead to reduced expenditure on bank staff [CASE STUDY 9] and more appropriate use of bank nurse time.[59]

District nursing 'out of hours'

170. In most trusts, district nursing services operate between 8 or 8.30 in the morning and 5 or 5.30 in the evening, five days a week. However, the need for nursing care extends beyond these timebands and so trusts have to make arrangements for district nursing services to be provided 'out of hours' – that is, in the evening, at night and at weekends. Even with these arrangements, there can be gaps in the provision of nursing care which may mean unnecessary hospital admissions, delayed hospital discharges, raised levels of GP call-out and, above all, a failure to respond to patient needs. But in some places, it is becoming increasingly difficult to recruit staff, particularly qualified district nurses, for the service. Shift patterns are unpopular and, on-call payments are unattractive.

171. The Audit Commission's survey of trusts found that up to midnight, 57 per cent of trusts in England and Wales have staff on duty in the evening across the trust, while the others have a mixture of on-call arrangements (5 per cent) or a combination of on-call and dedicated services (38 per cent). But these services are not necessarily available in all areas [BOX M] and they do not necessarily reflect any current assessment of need. As a result, patients in some places are admitted to residential or nursing homes, and even to hospital, for care that could be, and in some places is, provided at home.

CASE STUDY 9

Delegated budgets for bank staff

Three years ago, Northumberland Community Health NHS Trust replaced three locality banks with a central bank of 160 staff. Since April 1997, notional budgets for short-term bank cover have been delegated to team level. Bank budgets are set at 4 per cent of the district nursing team budget – a total of £217,576 across the trust. Half of this is managed for long-term bank cover (sickness of more than one month, maternity leave, training in excess of seven days and vacant posts). Teams get a monthly report on the number of requests made, the cover provided, costs and budget balance.

Actual short-term bank expenditure in 1997/98 (£63,097) was 58 per cent down on the budgeted figure and 39 of the 46 participating practices were underspent on their short-term budget. As a first-year incentive the underspends were retained by district nurses to purchase syringe drivers, various items for treatment rooms and moving and handling equipment.

Source: Audit Commission study site

BOX M

Out-of-hours service provision

In one trust visited by the Commission, none of the seven areas had the same out-of-hours service provision:

Area	Service hours	On-call duty
A	19.00-22.00	17.30-08.30
B	19.00-22.00	17.00-08.30
C	19.00-00.00	None
D	19.00-23.00	None
E (Mon-Fri)	None	17.00-08.00
E (Sat-Sun)	None	13.00 -08.00
F	None	None
G	None	None

Source: Audit Commission study site

172. After midnight, the pattern of provision changes again. Thirty-two per cent of trusts have no service, while the proportion with a dedicated trust-wide service drops to 29 per cent [EXHIBIT 30].

EXHIBIT 30

Evening and night service provision

After midnight almost one-third of trusts have no service.

Service provision before/after midnight

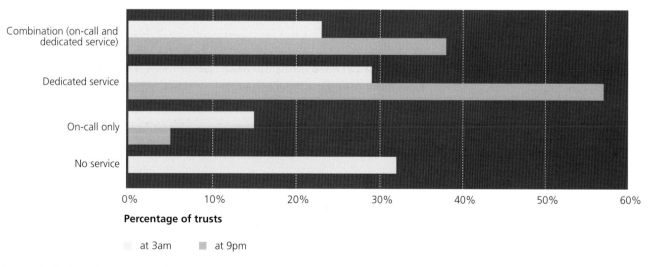

Percentage of trusts

at 3am   at 9pm

Source: Audit Commission survey of trusts

Lack of integration can lead to poor continuity of care.

173. Out-of-hours services face many of the same problems as daytime services. There tend to be no clear service objectives and few have referral criteria. As a result, daytime services may not be clear whom they should refer, and what they can expect, from the evening or night service. Referrals may be inappropriate because there is no referral protocol and no referral form, and because referrals are made mainly via answerphone or via another service (for example, the ambulance service or the local hospital trust) and referral information is often inadequate. Equally, care plans tend to be drawn up by the daytime staff (who, in most trusts, carry continuing 24-hour responsibility for patients seen in the evening or night) with no, or little, communication with evening or night-time staff. For example, it may not be known what drugs, dressings and other equipment the out-of-hours staff carry.

174. Some shift patterns provide no opportunity for communication between evening/night and day staff. Lack of integration can lead to poor continuity of care. Day staff need to be made aware of overnight changes in patients' conditions and any new referrals, while evening staff may lack knowledge of new patients and are seldom able to discuss them with the referring GP. Unlike the daytime district nurses, those working on evening or night services are not GP-attached; rather, they tend to work in localities or in geographical zones that may cut across the trust's locality structure. With small teams and scattered patient populations, this can mean that staff spend a substantial proportion of their time travelling. In one study site, more than one-third (36 per cent) of the hours worked in the evening and at night were accounted for by travel. Lack of contact with the GP is particularly problematic if there has to be a change to medication or some other aspect of care.

Grade-mix

175. The number of staff working on evening and night services is comparatively small; teams often consist of one district nursing sister and one or two nursing auxiliaries.[60] And the grade-mix is more dilute than in the daytime. Nursing auxiliaries account for up to two-thirds of the staff on duty, reflecting the fact that these services often had their origins in helping to put dependent people to bed at night.

176. But with the implementation of the Community Care Act, many of these 'put-to-bed' patients have been transferred to home-care services. Where this has occurred, there has been a sharp drop in the number of visits by staff on the evening service. One trust identified a drop of 28 per cent in the number of evening visits over a 12-month period. The speed with which this reduction has been achieved varies and, in some places, a few 'put-to-bed' patients remain on the district nursing caseload. The composition of teams does not necessarily reflect this change in patient profiles.

177. The numbers of staff on duty at the weekend are also much lower than in the week (85 per cent at one trust visited). But, in contrast, weekend services are mostly provided by registered staff nurses and qualified district nurses [EXHIBIT 31] who work on a rotational basis.[61] This mix of staff is more expensive, especially as pay rates are increased at the weekend. And it is not clear why the mix of daytime weekend services should be any different from the daytime weekday service.

Pre-planned work

178. Unlike the out-of-hours general medical service workload, which is dominated by emergency contacts, most evening and night district nursing work is pre-planned, providing care (for example, medication, dressings, palliative and diabetic care) on a frequent basis to a small group of patients. At one study site, 66 per cent of contacts by the evening service were for 'general care – including return to bed', 13 per cent were coded as 'eye care', and 7 per cent as 'medication'. At the same trust, just over half the contacts by the night service staff were coded as 'general care – including return to bed'. Emergency visits (for example, blocked catheters) form a comparatively small proportion of the workload. A review at another trust found that only 6 per cent of visits were unplanned (although they accounted for nearly 10 per cent of the time spent on direct care).

EXHIBIT 31

District nursing staff mix – weekdays, evenings/nights and weekends

There is a more expensive grade-mix on duty at the weekends.

Grade-mix on duty

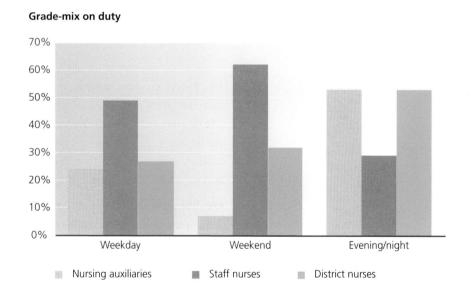

Source: Audit Commission diary exercises

...it is inappropriate to have staff nurses and auxiliaries working alone at the weekend or at night...

179. Some of the clinical work which qualified district nurses undertake out of hours could be, and in some trusts is being, done by community staff nurses **[BOX N]**. For example, in one trust, 13 per cent of G grade patient contact time was delivering 'general nursing care', and a further 6 per cent was spent on 'changing or checking dressings'. And G grades spent as much of their contact time (40 per cent) on care of the dying as did D grades.

180. The problem for trusts is that, while it is inefficient to have qualified district nurses undertaking general nursing care, it is also inappropriate to have staff nurses and auxiliaries working alone at the weekend or at night when other support services are less likely to be available.

Improving services

181. To provide a high-quality and efficient service to patients who need out-of-hours nursing care, trusts need to re-examine the use of the service, and to match shift patterns more closely to needs, provide peer support and enable more integrated working. Some trusts are trying to form strong links with GP out-of-hours services to provide an element of peer support and enable more integrated working **[CASE STUDY 10]**.

BOX N

Review of weekend working

Similar issues of efficiency arise at the weekend. One trust's internal review of weekend working concluded that:

- the majority of visits carried out at the weekend could be done by community staff nurses rather than by qualified district nurses;

- the number of visits made did not require staff to work all day;

- during the week, many staff were working in excess of their contracted hours; and

- bank nurses were used to cover for nurses who had worked the weekend and were taking time off in lieu.

Source: Audit Commission study site

CASE STUDY 10

Integrating weekend, evening and night services

Until recently, district nursing staff in Bradford Community NHS Trust worked on a rotational basis at the weekend, visiting patients on their own, and others', caseloads. Staff who worked the weekend took time off in lieu during the week. GP fundholders were concerned that their attached staff were unavailable during the week and could not liaise effectively with the rest of the primary healthcare team. At the same time, much of the nursing resource on the evening and night service was providing social care – for example, putting people to bed.

In January 1996, the trust started an integrated weekend, evening and night service. Referral criteria were established for the new service, focusing on patients who would require hospital admission if nursing care were unavailable in the community. Patients who required social care were transferred to social services. The new service has 92 staff and some of the salary costs for the new team were covered by savings on the payment of weekend enhancements under the old system.

The integrated out-of-hours service has established good links with the primary care service based in a nearby office. This is a partnership between the deputising medical service and the trust's nurses who provide telephone health advice to patients out of hours. Deputising GPs or the 'telephone' nurses can refer to the district nursing service if an urgent home visit is required, based on the new referral criteria. Conversely, district nurses can refer patients to, or seek advice from, the GPs.

Source: Audit Commission trust visit

A few trusts have decided that the concept of 'out of hours' is redundant...

182. A few trusts have decided that the concept of 'out of hours' is redundant because it reflects the way in which nurses are employed, and paid, rather than patients' needs for care. Some of these trusts are trying to improve co-ordination by integrating the provision of day and evening services **[CASE STUDY 11]**.

183. If district nursing is going to provide an emergency service and care for patients with complex needs whenever these arise, then it will have to staff these services with more community staff nurses. And trusts will need to create a clear leadership role for qualified district nurses to provide support and supervision to these staff as well as making high-level clinical decisions when these are required. In order to staff these services more efficiently, trusts also need to re-examine the structure of on-call and call-out payments.

CASE STUDY 11

Improving co-ordination

In Community Healthcare Bolton NHS Trust the integration of the day and evening shifts has been a long-standing aim to meet changing patient needs. The existing town-centre-based team of evening shift staff have no links with the GP practices, with other professional groups or other agencies. Analysis of data for September 1997 found that 82 per cent of patients were seen prior to 10pm. By moving to a 9pm finish, the Trust can deploy a greater number of staff at peak times and provide new services, such as evening treatment-room sessions – a response to demands from patients who may be dependent for transport on a working adult or working in the daytime themselves. A pilot project has been set up, with day staff extending their shift into the evening, while evening staff shorten their shift or extend into days.

Benefits of integration include:

- improved continuity of care – patients are cared for by one team;
- better communications with other members of the primary healthcare team;
- use of shared records;
- reduced waiting time in the evening for patients;
- access to training for all staff;
- reduced risk of staff being out alone late at night; and
- more flexible working hours for staff.

Potential savings include:

- reduced travel costs – because teams are locally based and some patients are seen in treatment rooms; and
- lower staff costs – because shifts finish at 9pm rather than 11pm.

Source: Audit Commission study site

Clinics

184. The principal aim of district nursing services is to organise and deliver the nursing care that is necessary to support patients in their own homes, or in residential accommodation, for as long as possible. But such care is expensive to provide and resources need to be targeted effectively. In some cases, the objective can be achieved more efficiently and more effectively when care is delivered away from the patient's home.

185. There are two types of district nursing clinic:

- general clinics – which may operate an appointment system, or be run as 'drop-in' times – provide things such as venepuncture, health promotion and management of chronic illnesses; and

- specialist clinics – often established by specialists nurses, these cover activities such as leg ulcer management and continence care.

186. National data show that the level of contacts in clinics has remained almost unchanged (at 6 per cent) throughout the 1990s. But the proportion of contacts recorded in clinics varies widely between trusts, from none to 38 per cent [**EXHIBIT 32**]. Within trusts there can be considerable differences between teams in the proportion of contacts that take place in clinics.

EXHIBIT 32

Proportion of contacts in health centres and GP premises

The proportion of contacts in clinics varies widely.

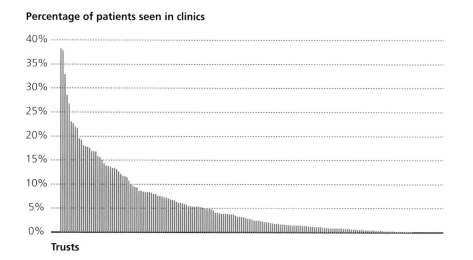

Percentage of patients seen in clinics

Trusts

Source: Audit Commission survey of trusts

Some trusts actively encourage district nurses to promote clinics as a way of increasing efficiency and effectiveness.

187. Generally speaking, cost per contact falls as the proportion of contacts in clinics rises [EXHIBIT 33]. The lower cost per contact is achieved by cutting travel costs and time, reducing the average contact time, increasing the number of contacts made and making more use of lower-graded staff. But there are travel costs for patients, and trusts need to examine whether it is cost-effective to provide transport for those attending clinics to ensure sufficient patient numbers.

188. Cost per contact in clinics can vary considerably, depending on patient throughput and clinic staffing. At one study site trust, where 10 per cent of patient contact was provided in clinics, qualified district nurses accounted for only 11 per cent of the clinic hours worked. At another trust, where 20 per cent of contact time was spent in clinics, qualified district nurses provided 42 per cent of the clinic hours worked.

189. Some trusts actively encourage district nurses to promote clinics as a way of increasing efficiency and effectiveness [CASE STUDY 12]. For patients who are mobile, attending clinics may be a more efficient way to organise their care. But among the trusts visited, the criteria for establishing clinics were not always clear and patients' views were not routinely sought. Often the decision was made at practice level without consideration of the wider picture and without a system for ensuring that patients are seen in the right place and by the right health professional. Trust managers did not know with any certainty what clinics were run where, when or why.

EXHIBIT 33

Staff cost per patient and proportion of contacts in clinics

As the proportion of contacts in clinics rise, cost per contact falls.

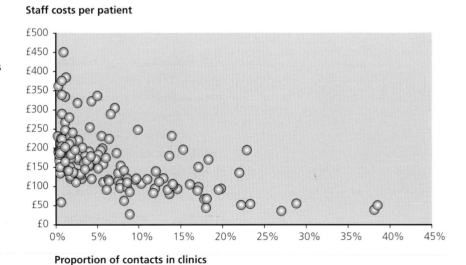

Staff costs per patient

Proportion of contacts in clinics

◯ Trusts

Source: Audit Commission survey of trusts

CASE STUDY 12

The cost-effectiveness of community leg ulcer clinics

A two-year randomised controlled trial involving 233 patients with venous leg ulcers in four community trusts was conducted in the Trent region. Trained nurses gave 123 patients weekly treatment using four-layer bandaging in eight community leg ulcer clinics. The remaining 113 patients were allocated to a control group and received the usual care at home from their district nursing service.

Twelve-month follow-up showed that the ulcers of patients in the clinic group tended to heal sooner than those in the control group. And the clinic group tended to experience fewer problems with their leg ulcer dressings in terms of infection, dressing pain and discomfort. The mean cost per clinic attendance was estimated at £29.92, compared with a mean cost per visit for patients in the control group of £10.55.

But clinic patients had an average of 20 ulcer-free weeks per year compared with 14 weeks in the control. Analysis of the cost per ulcer-free week showed that the clinic was more cost-effective. If patient throughput was increased to more than ten and the clinic was staffed with nurses up to E grade (rather than G and H), then the benefit could be obtained at reduced cost. However, patients have to spend additional time travelling to and from the clinic, and in waiting for and having treatment.

Source: Ref. 40

190. District nurses need routinely to question the location of care provided at the time of referral and assessment. It should also be considered as a part of regular caseload review. Currently the major factor determining whether a patient can be seen in a clinic is whether or not their practice operates clinics. This, in turn, is determined by the availability of suitable premises and the support of the GPs, rather than by the needs of the patients. Service managers need to put more effort into finding premises in which clinics can be provided.

191. Patients on a particular GP list are generally cared for by the nurses attached to that practice, using the facilities available in the practice. In most trusts, patients tend not to be seen at clinics held in other practices even when these have spare capacity. And low patient numbers can make some practice-based clinics inefficient. District nurses and managers need to tackle this mismatch of resources and demand by planning clinic services across local communities rather than by simply responding to the needs of individual practices.

192. In planning the development of clinic services, users' views need to be taken into account [BOX O]. In particular, care must be taken to ensure that increasing clinics does not reduce access to services for those who are housebound.

BOX O

Patients' views of clinics

Patients offered contrasting views about clinics. This 78-year-old lady attends a leg ulcer clinic: *'Well, I mean, while I'm able I would go to the clinic, but I mean there might come a time – lots of people can't get to the clinic, they've got no family to take them there... but while I'm able to I prefer going to the clinic.'* Another 83-year-old lady is collected for her clinic visits: *'Nurse K suggested that I went down for this 4-in-1 bandage to see if it would do me any good and I said I can't get there, she said don't worry about it, we'll fix up an ambulance, they're nice gents that come and collect you, and that's what happened. I like going to the clinic. The only thing I don't like about it is I have to get up extra early that morning.'*

But patients seen at home, when asked about going to the clinic, were less positive. Some felt that it would be very difficult to get there, particularly if they were reliant on public transport. Those who hadn't experienced clinic visits used hospital or surgery visits as a comparison: *'Well, I prefer the district nurses in the sense that I don't have to go trailing down to the hospital, you know you are at home, if you are waiting, you are waiting in your own premises, you're not sitting in a clinic looking at everyone... You have to explain everything, they don't know you, you don't know them...'*

Source: Audit Commission patients' and carers' study

RECOMMENDATIONS

4 Improving Service Efficiency

To improve efficiency and economy in staffing the service, trusts need to:

1 monitor grade-mix by comparing the work done with activities expected by grade of nurse

2 review the number and mix of staff deployed against patient needs at different times of day and different days of the week

3 examine non-patient activity and free district nurses' time to fulfil their role in clinical and team management

4 develop training and education programmes to support extended roles for community staff nurses and nursing auxiliaries

5 review the costs, use and activity of temporary nursing staff

6 create a centrally co-ordinated bank staff database and management service and ensure that bank staff have regular and consistent training

7 delegate nominal bank staff budgets to district nursing teams

Out-of-hours services would be more efficient and effective if trusts:

8 reviewed the need for, and provision of, district nursing services out of hours

9 considered the integration of day and evening services to improve service quality and cost-effectiveness

10 examined the potential to link district nursing evening and night services and out-of-hours medical services

Services could be more efficient if trusts made greater use of clinics:

11 by agreeing a policy that sets out the reasons for developing or extending the provision of clinic or treatment room sessions

12 by reviewing patient access to existing clinics, clinic throughput and resourcing

5

Moving Forward

This report sets out a challenging agenda for change.
The pressure on district nursing to deliver more for less will
not go away and trusts need to tackle some fundamental
problems if the efficiency, effectiveness and quality of
care being delivered are to improve. The establishment
of primary care groups (local health groups in Wales)
should provide a structure for tackling these issues.

Introduction

193. Many aspects of district nursing at the end of the 1990s would have been almost unthinkable just ten years ago: district nurses are managing complex treatments in the community which previously took place in hospital; palliative care and the nursing of terminally ill patients at home have become commonplace; patient dependency levels have risen overall. At the same time, the bathing and the putting-to-bed tasks have largely been transferred to home care services.

194. Equally, there are some important constants: the trust and confidence that patients and carers have in district nurses; the value that they place on being treated with humanity and kindness, on the feeling of being cared for and on having time to talk; the role played by district nurses in liaison with other agencies and health professionals in developing, implementing and managing the broader packages of care that can enable people to live in their own homes. These remain central.

195. But the pressure on district nursing, like that on home care services, GPs and others, to do more for less – to increase activity and to deliver safe, clinically effective care, at less cost – will not go away. In these circumstances, the temptation is for each service to redraw its boundaries and narrow its focus, becoming more task-focused and less patient-oriented. If it is to retain what users value, district nursing must resist this temptation.

196. This report has highlighted a series of problems with the basic building blocks of an efficient and effective district nursing service [BOX P]. Trusts need to tackle these basic problems if they are to improve the efficiency of the service and the quality of care delivered to patients.

BOX P

District nursing: tackling the basics

In order to improve the quality and efficiency of district nursing services, trusts – working with commissioners – need to tackle:

- the lack of clear service definition;

- the poor understanding of need for district nursing at a community level;

- confusion and uncertainty surrounding referrals;

- the poor quality of some referral information;

- the lack of regular caseload profiling;

- the mismatch between resources and patients' needs;

- barriers to working across professional and organisational boundaries;

- unwarranted variations in the quality of clinical performance;

- the lack of quality monitoring and the limited acceptance of clinical supervision;

- low levels of involvement in clinical audit;

- inappropriate use of clinical nurse specialists;

- limited delegation of clinical work to community staff nurses;

- insufficient time spent by district nurses on patient management;

- inequitable and inefficient service provision out of hours; and

- the ad hoc development of clinic-based services.

197. Many of the recommendations made in this report are not new. Recommendations that concern the need to match supply with demand for close and good working arrangements between health and social care for systematic and regular caseload review; and for evaluation of quality, have been made before.

198. But further, substantial challenges are in train which raise fundamental questions about what kind of service will be needed and how it should be managed. This final chapter sets out to:

- examine the challenges that lie ahead for district nursing;
- consider the future management of the service; and
- explore the opportunities that emanate from the new policy framework for tackling the problems.

Challenges facing the service

199. The challenge of 'modernising' the service should not be underestimated; it will be difficult. There are four main challenges:

- responding to changes in patient needs;
- coping with rising patient expectations;
- developing competencies to provide services away from hospital settings; and
- staffing the service.

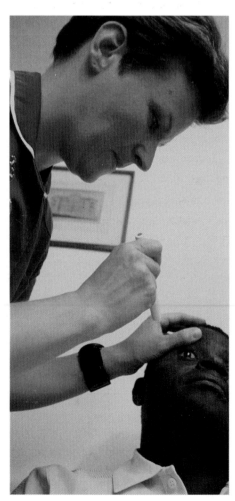

Responding to changes in patient needs

200. The first of these challenges concerns the changing needs of patients. Although the population of elderly people is growing, their healthcare needs are evolving. In the future, there is likely to be greater emphasis on providing health education and advice to enable people to maintain their health and independence for as long as possible. Early intervention can prevent deterioration that could otherwise lead to increased disability, dependence and pressure on health and social care budgets. District nurses could play a key role in identifying risk and detecting early signs of conditions associated with ageing such as stroke, Parkinson's disease, arthritis and diabetes.

Coping with rising patient expectations

201. Patients' expectations – with respect to quality of service, timeliness and standards of communication – are likely to continue to rise, as are expectations of the kinds of care that they can get. Healthcare will increasingly be concerned with achieving the best possible quality of life for patients and their carers and with meeting preferences for palliative and terminal care at home (Ref. 41). For example, although most terminally ill people spend the greater part of their last year of life at home, and would prefer to die there, the majority still actually die in a hospital or hospice. If the service is to respond to the wishes of service-users, then it will need to provide more community nursing around the clock. And it is likely that much of the care required will be organised by district nursing services [CASE STUDY 13].

Flintshire Complementary Care Service

Out-of-hours nursing for terminally ill patients was provided at Clwydian Community Care NHS Trust by a combination of on-call district nursing staff, Marie Curie nurses and agency nurses. These arrangements were viewed as unsatisfactory because:

- terminally ill patients were being admitted unnecessarily to hospital and hospice;
- there were delayed hospital discharges for terminally ill patients;
- poor communication between the agency and the trust were not uncommon – for example, incidents where the patient had died but the district nurses had not been informed;
- there was discontinuity of carer – it was not uncommon to find different agency nurses visiting a patient each day;
- the trust was unable to supervise the quality of care that was provided and had no input to the training of agency staff;
- the cost of agency nursing input was comparatively high; and

- the provision of Marie Curie services could not be guaranteed.

In March 1997, the Trust set up a pilot project, with additional funding from the health authority, to create a bank of registered and unregistered nurses who would provide continuing care for patients out of hours in Flintshire, and to purchase any special equipment needed. The service has clear criteria for admission. These are:

- children with life-threatening or chronic degenerative conditions, who require medium- to long-term nursing intervention;
- adults with a chronic or acute medical condition who require nursing interventions, such as enteral feeding; and
- terminally ill patients who require care over and above what the Marie Curie Service can provide.

In its first four months, staff provided 28 nights of care for 11 patients. Ten of the eleven patients were diagnosed with cancer and were at the terminal stage of their illness. In all cases, the patients were receiving care from the

district nursing service and the Marie Curie nursing service. The perceived benefits of the service included:

- preventing hospice or hospital admission in the last three days of life when the patient wanted to remain at home;
- speedier discharge from hospital or hospice where full nursing care was needed at short notice;
- meeting the wishes of patients and their families to remain at home;
- improving communications through the liaison between bank and district nursing staff;
- less stress for community staff whose patients required continuing nursing care, as they had immediate access to a nursing resource;
- ensuring that bank staff had the same training as other staff, thus promoting the same standard of care for patients; and
- making salary cost savings by replacing agency nurses at £110 per shift with bank staff at £80 per shift.

Source: Audit Commission study site

...a highly skilled and experienced workforce is needed to deliver the service of the future...

Adjusting to evolving hospital services

202. The notion of what hospitals are for is likely to become narrower and more focused on high-tech diagnosis and care. More healthcare needs will be met without recourse to hospital admission, and technical ability to provide services away from hospital settings will continue to grow, including areas of clinical investigation. The part which district nurses play in the continuum of care will need to evolve as these changes occur in hospital services. New services can be, and in some trusts already are being, provided by district nursing [CASE STUDY 14]. There will be a range of alternatives to acute hospital admission (such as, hospital-at-home, and rapid response schemes) and intermediate care facilities focused on rehabilitation and enabling patients to return home. But whether these needs are met by district nursing depends on shifting budgets in the system as a whole. Commissioning by PCGs/LHGs allows for such changes in funding.

Staffing the service

203. In the past, cost-based factors have pushed trusts towards employing 'cheaper' staff mixes and the number, and proportion, of qualified district nurses has reduced. But greater intensity and complexity of patient needs and the demands of organising and managing complex care packages will act to slow, even reverse, these trends. In many places district nursing traditionally had comparatively low levels of staff turnover and vacant posts. But the recognition that a highly skilled and experienced workforce is needed to deliver the service of the future will coincide with a substantial rise in the numbers of staff leaving through retirement. The challenge of training and recruiting a district nursing workforce for the future will have to be faced.

Managing the service

204. Managing staff in the community is different from managing them in other settings, mainly because managers cannot easily check what practitioners are doing. If managers are going to be responsible for the quality of clinical care, then they must have processes in place for examining and assessing the clinical practice of staff. They also need to demonstrate that someone, other than the nurses themselves, knows what they are doing and is monitoring the quality of care that they are delivering to patients.

205. Using the assessment of patients with leg ulcers and continence problems, this report has identified a range of performance with failures in the standards of care at one end and exemplars at the other. But the process of learning lessons from each of these extremes is not well developed. Clinical governance underlines the importance of tackling these problems and emphasises the urgency of putting in place standards and systems for audit. The requirement placed on NHS trust and PCG/LHG boards to be accountable for the quality of care that nurses deliver means that their practice will be more exposed to scrutiny by others than before.

CASE STUDY 14

Home blood transfusions in Bolton

Community Healthcare Bolton NHS Trust has established a home blood transfusion service so that acute or terminally ill patients do not have frequent, disruptive and costly admissions to hospital for the transfusion of blood or platelets. The consultant haematologist works closely with the team to identify suitable patients (typical conditions include AIDS or AIDS-related complex; anaemia due to chronic renal disease; haemoglobinopathies; and chronic gastrointestinal bleeding). The community trust and its nursing team are responsible for ensuring that staff are trained appropriately in cannulation, transfusion, advanced basic life support and the treatment of anaphylaxis. The service can be provided at a time of day best suited to the patient's health status – rather than the hospital routine. Early evidence suggests that there are cost savings. The cost of home blood transfusion is £115 per completed patient episode, compared with the cost of an occupied bed day in hospital which averages £200.

CASE HISTORY

Mrs A was terminally ill. She needed a blood transfusion to relieve anaemia and wanted to die at home with her family around her. Hospice staff had been unable to provide the transfusion because of her poor veins and Mrs A had requested that she should not be admitted to hospital. The rapid response team visited her at home on Saturday afternoon within 20 minutes of her referral. She was unable to stand, was drowsy, could not drink fluids unaided and believed her death was imminent. The nurses were able to cannulate and transfuse two units of blood in the afternoon. Nurses continued to visit throughout the evening, making a final visit at 11pm.

Mrs A's condition improved dramatically overnight and the team found her sitting up in bed drinking tea. A further two units were transfused in the morning, after which Mrs A was able to stand, to transfer from bed to chair independently, eat and drink with only minimal assistance. Care was transferred to the normal district nursing service.

Source: Audit Commission study site

206. Trusts need to have people and processes in place for carrying out the key management functions highlighted in the report: developing and communicating referral criteria; scrutinising activity and profiling caseloads; examining resource allocation across teams; and identifying professional development needs. Most importantly, trusts should be developing the management skills of district nurses. And then they should delegate, with appropriate levels of support, as much as possible so that teams can become self-managed. Trusts need to invest in professional development programmes to improve key skills within teams – for example, budget management, collective-decision making, communications, action planning, principles of teamwork, recruitment and selection, and performance management. Trusts also need to provide a facilitator who can help teams to identify their development needs, and who can support and develop the role of team co-ordinators [CASE STUDY 15]. Facilitators also have a role in helping teams to overcome inter-personal problems within the team.

CASE STUDY 15

Developing team co-ordinators

Bradford Community Health NHS Trust started to develop self-managed integrated teams in November 1995. Each team has selected a co-ordinator from among the district nursing, health visiting or practice nursing staff. Two team facilitators have responsibility for developing self-managed teams and providing ongoing support for the team co-ordinators. Typically, team co-ordinators meet once a month with the facilitators. The position of team co-ordinator is reviewed annually by the team facilitators to identify whether the position should be rotated to another team member and whether team objectives have been achieved.

In addition to their clinical caseload, the team co-ordinators are responsible for co-ordinating and managing:

- team budgets, including salary costs for the trust's nurses, supplies and dressings, and staff development;

- skills audit to identify expertise, as well as the gaps, in knowledge or experience within the team;

- how any gaps in knowledge or experience can be filled;

- the dissemination of clinical knowledge and good practice;

- needs assessment of the practice population;

- objective-setting for identified needs for nursing care;

- consistent standards of practice across members of the team by developing standards and guidelines for practice; and

- poor performance of team members.

Training is given to team co-ordinators in order that they can fulfil this role. The one-week programme covers new areas of policy (for example, the introduction of PCGs), recruitment and selection, budget management, performance management, team motivation, conflict management and objective setting. This training programme is also available to other community staff as part of their learning and development.

Source: Audit Commission trust visit

...district nurses can be out of sight and out of mind...

207. Conventionally, community nurses have operated in distinct roles (district nurse, health visitor, practice nurse or school nurse), supported by nurse managers in a hierarchical structure. Practice nurses are generally employed by GPs (although this separation will disappear with primary care trusts – PCTs). These structures have tended to encourage nurses' allegiance to their specialist roles and to distinguish them from other nursing and medical colleagues. In some trusts, there is an extensive management hierarchy with several layers between the district nurse and the trust board. In others, the structure is completely flat with no one between the district nurses and the executive director on the board. Both structures present problems.

208. In the hierarchical structure, district nurses may report to a community services manager, who in turn reports to a locality manager – in many cases, neither of these types of manager has a nursing background. The locality manager may be responsible for staff from several different professional backgrounds and up to 30 district nursing teams, dispersed across a substantial geographic area. In the flatter structure, district nurses can also be out of sight and out of mind – they are poorly supported and their work is not systematically reviewed. A district nursing service that is both responsive to the changing needs of patients and the pressures to improve economy, efficiency and effectiveness will require different approaches to managing the service that are less about structure and more about carrying out management functions effectively.

209. New models of organisation, in particular integrated nursing teams, are being tried in many parts of the country. Integrated nursing teams have been defined as *'a team of community-based nurses from different disciplines, working together within a primary care setting pooling their skills, knowledge and ability in order to provide the most effective care for their patients within a practice and the community it covers'* (Ref. 42).

210. District nurses working as part of integrated teams identify various benefits [BOX Q, overleaf]. Integrating nursing teams enables more innovative ways of delivering nursing services. Where these teams work, it is because they break down the barriers between professional groups. Some of these barriers – for example, the fact that practice nurses are employed by GPs – will dissolve with PCTs. But integration should facilitate improved co-ordination with social care and the voluntary sector.

BOX Q

Benefits of integrated nursing teams

- peer group (including cross-profession) support – for example, opportunities to discuss patient care issues and to share knowledge about clinical procedures;

- shared aims and objectives linked to those of the practice;

- improved communications between team members and with GPs;

- services that focus more on the health needs assessment of the local population – rather than the caseloads of individual nurses;

- shared protocols that lead to more consistent care delivery and advice;

- increased understanding of each other's roles and an emphasis within the community nursing team on expertise and skills rather than traditional roles;

- improvements in efficiency (for example, in the past the district nurse might have visited a patient in the morning only to find the patient was going to see the practice nurse in the afternoon);

- multidisciplinary or cross-functional use of nursing auxiliaries or healthcare assistants;

- more cross-team referrals (for example, between district nurses and practice nurses) with fewer nurses involved in each episode of care for people with complex needs;

- more collaborative working across professional boundaries (for example, sharing responsibility for vaccinations and immunisations) to give patients improved access to services; and

- an emphasis on leadership rather than hierarchical structures and autocratic management.

Source: Audit Commission, interviews at study sites

211. The Audit Commission's survey of district nurses found consistent differences between those in integrated nursing teams and those in conventional district nursing teams.[62] A higher proportion of nurses in integrated teams were involved in profiling the health needs of their local community or practice population than nurses in conventional teams. Moreover, those in integrated teams undertook this profiling in association with other community nurses and practice nurses as well as with non-nursing staff. Higher proportions were also involved in developing and ensuring clinical standards.

212. Staff in integrated teams consistently reported that they were well supported by management, that they felt well informed about developments in their trust and that their views were taken into account. Fewer reported getting conflicting job requests, while formal meetings with health visitors, practice nurses, GPs and social workers were more common.[63]

213. These survey findings echo the impressions of tangible achievement made by some integrated teams in resolving previously intractable problems, improving communication and collaboration (Ref. 43), and making efficiency gains [CASE STUDY 16]. A recently published literature review (Ref. 44) identified only two research-based evaluations,[64] but independent evaluations are increasingly demonstrating that important benefits in management, and in nursing practice, can result from the development of integrated teams.[65]

CASE STUDY 16

The Nettleham experiment

Nettleham is a split-site total purchasing pilot practice covering 10,000 patients within a semi-rural area of nine villages near Lincoln. The aim of the Nettleham experiment was fourfold:

- to form an integrated nursing team;
- to improve communications within and across the primary healthcare team;
- to encourage professional development of the nurses; and
- to ensure effective use of the management resources.

The nursing resources and associated management structures were reorganised in April 1994 and a district nurse was appointed as nurse team leader.

Changes to management processes

- monthly meetings between district nurses, general practitioners and practice manager to review nursing team activity;
- joint standard-setting and protocol-development meetings between district nurses and practice nurses were introduced;
- joint training sessions for all nursing staff;
- practice nurses and district nurses making entries directly into patients' practice records;
- GPs making notes on district nursing patient records; and
- district nurses making entries to patient information held on practice computer.

Changes in nursing practice

- E & F grade district nursing staff make initial assessments as well as team leader;
- clinic has been established in a residential home;
- district nurses are raising awareness of nurses' roles and taking direct referrals;
- increasing amount of nursing time is being spent in bereavement support, patient teaching and counselling – supporting the view that the nursing service is beginning to become more patient-focused;
- level of referrals between district and practice nurses is improving; and
- there is no significant rise in the proportion of time spent by district nurses in non-patient-related activity.

Source: Audit Commission visit to practice

...in most trusts, only a handful of district nurses are working in integrated teams.

214. The development of integrated nursing teams may be accompanied by the introduction of practice-based management in which teams take responsibility for delegated budgets from the trust. These self-managed teams may also be responsible for recruitment and selection, changing skill-mix, influencing budget-setting, managing attendance and identifying training needs. And there is no evidence that this reduces the amount of time that staff spend on patient care.[66] Self-managing teams offer potential savings from reduced management staff costs. But, in practice, few trusts have yet realised any savings because most self-managed teams are run as pilot schemes alongside conventional locality management structures.

215. The promotion of self-management skills and the development of integrated nursing teams are welcome steps towards a nursing workforce that is more proactive and responsive to change. But they are not easy options and they pose a number of challenges.

216. Research (Refs. 43 and 45) suggests that the development of integrated teams takes longer than anticipated and is frequently problematic because:

- some groups perceive themselves to be working already in what they consider to be an effective team and see no added benefits;

- nurses may want to form an integrated nursing team but lack the support of their GP(s);

- nurses may feel that their workload is such that they are reluctant to take on additional responsibilities;

- integrated nursing teams may not be suitable for nurses serving single-handed practices; and

- nurses may perceive teamworking as the development of generic community nursing which threatens their specialist role.

217. The introduction of integrated nursing teams is best done where it is incremental, and is based on teams opting in [CASE STUDY 17].

218. The idea that community and practice nurses should work together in multidisciplinary teams has been periodically advocated by both government and professional organisations for more than 30 years.[67] Half the trusts responding to the Audit Commission's survey report that they have some integrated nursing teams. But, in most trusts, only a handful of district nurses are working in integrated teams. What is different now is that there are good examples around to demonstrate that it is possible and from which others can learn. The emphasis on quality in *The new NHS – Modern and Dependable*, and the objectives of PCGs/LHGs, create the right environment for making the changes.

CASE STUDY 17

Integrated nursing teams: the Sheffield approach

Community Health Sheffield NHS Trust began developing integrated nursing teams in February 1995. By November 1997, 30 teams had been established and the number of service managers reduced by 14.

The key features of the approach included:

- teams should be practice-attached and, ideally, based within the practice;

- prospective teams opt in to the initiative rather than team formation being prescribed;

- one full-time and two part-time facilitators were appointed to market the idea and provide ongoing support to newly established teams; an active marketing strategy was established to promote the concept through workshops and meetings with prospective teams;

- the tier of clinical nurse managers was reduced as teams became self-managing;

- a professional development facilitator provided monthly developmental workshops;

- ongoing support by the facilitator was made available to the teams;

- each team was required to identify a team co-ordinator to facilitate communication between team members and the wider primary healthcare team;

- monthly meetings were organised by the facilitators for the team co-ordinators;

- established teams were encouraged to take responsibility for the community nursing budget for the practice;

- teams were encouraged to undertake health needs assessments of their practice populations; and

- teams were expected to establish shared objectives.

Source: Ref. 43

Boundaries with social services

219. The boundaries between health and social services continue to prevent services from best meeting the needs of those who use them. The most dependent of district nursing patients – those with complex health and social needs – are most likely to suffer as a consequence, often having

...users and carers can experience...frustration about the way that care is provided.

to deal with several different agencies. The Audit Commission's review of caseloads has shown that up to 40 per cent of district nursing patients are also receiving some form of social care. But users and carers can experience:

• confusion about how to obtain the services that meet their needs because of uncertainty and dispute over which service should provide care, which is due to a lack of role definition and clear referral criteria for the different services;

• anxiety about what care they will receive, how it will be provided and who will pay, due to conflicting messages, duplication and gaps in assessments by different staff, who are often not co-ordinated effectively; and

• frustration about the way that care is provided, and the number of different agencies coming into their homes due to ineffective communication between these agencies.

220. Implementation of the community care part of the NHS and Community Care Act in 1993 had a major impact on district nursing workloads. The shift of personal care from health to social services has been significant but not always planned adequately or implemented appropriately. Care for some people with complex needs is managed entirely by social services staff, often with no input from the health service until a crisis arises. The shift of responsibility to social services has happened at different rates across the country. In some areas, district nursing services still provide a high level of personal care to patients while, in others, most personal care is provided by social services even where there are identified health needs.

A range of models has emerged for care management.

221. *Caring for People* (Ref. 46) envisioned care management and joint assessment as the cornerstones of high quality care. The care manager is responsible for assessing and co-ordinating the care for individual 'care managed' patients with complex health and social needs. But research on the role of community nurses as care managers shows that their involvement varied widely (Ref. 47). A range of models has emerged for care management, reflecting the way in which community trusts and local social services authorities have developed their services, either jointly or independently. For example:

- one study site trust covered the same area as two social services authorities. In one part, the care manager role was performed by five qualified district nurses who were funded by the social services authority. The other social services authority funded one post with a responsibility for dealing solely with continuing care clients;

- at another study site, a continuing care liaison nurse post is funded by the health authority. The postholder is responsible for assessing patients who require extensive packages of care at home or nursing home care. Assessments are undertaken jointly with a care manager from social services to identify health and social care needs and to agree the lead responsibility for particular aspects of care. Where there are clear complex healthcare needs, the continuing care liaison nurse will take the assessment forward to the health authority for continuing care funding. Where the emphasis is on social needs, the care manager takes the assessment forward; and

- at a third trust, district nurses are not care managers, but may be involved in joint assessments at the request of social services.

222. In many places the system of care management has become a barrier to good teamwork between district nurses and social services staff. And where care managers assess need and purchase care from private agencies, there may be no direct liaison between the care manager and the district nurse.

223. The consultation document, *Partnership in Action* (in Wales, *Partnership for Improvement*), sets out to promote increased co-operation between health and social services (Refs. 13 and 14). The proposals should provide an opportunity for trusts to:

- better define the role of the district nursing service and its objectives;

- agree these objectives with local social services authorities and agree how social care needs will be met so as to ensure that there are no gaps or duplication in service;

- establish and agree clear criteria for referrals and how they will be dealt with;

- agree clear criteria and procedures for assessments to ensure that the plan for future care is developed with minimal conflict and in a way that reassures users of the service; and

- ensure that service provision 'on the ground' is co-ordinated so that users receive care from the right provider at the right time.

Many trusts and social services authorities have sought to co-ordinate services and work together more effectively...

224. Many trusts and social services authorities have sought to co-ordinate services and work together more effectively to deliver better integrated, user-centred health and social care [CASE STUDY 18], but even the most innovative have been restricted by the current legislative framework.

225. *Partnership in Action* (Ref. 13) proposes to provide legislation for pooled budgets, lead commissioners and integrated provision. Pooled budgets would enable health and social services to pool their resources, which should allow staff at an operational level to provide integrated packages of care. Under the arrangements for lead commissioners, one authority (health or social services) would be able to transfer funds and delegate functions to a second, so that it could commission both heath and social services. The lead commissioner could focus on the health and social needs of patients and users. This user-centred approach should help to ensure that the most appropriate type of care is purchased. Further integration of services would be possible under proposals for greater freedoms for NHS trusts to provide social care. A single provider of care may be able to better co-ordinate services to the benefit of patients.

CASE STUDY 18

An example of a joint operational policy for home care and district nursing developed to improve service provision

A health authority, community trust and two social services authorities worked collaboratively to produce a joint operational policy for district nursing and home care. All of the agencies involved recognise the need for joint collaboration in both the planning and the delivery of current and future district nursing and local authority home care services. While the initiative aims to at improve joint planning and service commissioning, the first priority is to help the staff that provide frontline services to establish effective ways of working together for the benefit of service users.

Documentation was produced to provide a framework to help district nurses, home care managers and care managers to make decisions when planning and providing care. Patients of the district nursing service are entered into one of six care packages that reflect the overall objective of the care – that is, curative, palliative, rehabilitation, self-care promotion and maintenance (low- and high-risk). Identified within each care programme is the agency that has lead responsibility for providing the category of care – for example, palliative care is a health responsibility and low-risk maintenance is a social services responsibility. The range of activities to be provided by each service individually and collaboratively is outlined in the joint operational policy for each care programme.

Joint guidelines also outline the responsibilities of each agency in respect of specific activities, and these are supported by individual policies covering these activities that have been adopted by social services departments and the trust.

Source: Audit Commission study site

The new policy framework

226. The new policy environment created by *The new NHS – Modern and Dependable* (Ref. 10) and the consultation document, *Partnership in Action* (Ref. 13), provide a framework that will put the onus on trusts, together with commissioners and their partners in local authorities, to place district nursing in the context of other services provided locally. Together they must tackle the fundamental question: what is the district nursing service for? Only then will it be possible to answer questions about the level of need and how district nursing services should be developed locally.

Primary care groups/local health groups

227. The establishment of PCGs in England (and LHGs in Wales) provide district nurses with an unprecedented opportunity to influence the shape of future community nursing services and a structure for tackling the issues of inefficiency and inequity described in this report. The ways in which district nursing is represented on PCGs/LHGs will therefore be crucial.

228. The purpose of PCGs is to *'enable GPs, community nurses and other health and social care professionals to improve the health of their community and the delivery of care to patients'* (Ref. 48). They have three main functions [BOX R]. These are:

- improving the health of, and addressing health inequalities in, their community;

- developing primary care and community services across the PCG; and

- advising on, or commissioning directly, a range of hospital services for patients within their area that meets patients' needs appropriately.

BOX R

Primary care group functions

PCGs have three main functions:

Improving the health of, and addressing health inequalities in, their community through:

- the identification of the health needs of their community

- contributing to and informing the development of the local HImP

- working closely with social services (and other local government agencies), to ensure the co-ordination and integration of service delivery

- the involvement of the public in the work of the group so as to inform the delivery of appropriate services

cont./

BOX R (cont.)

Developing primary care and community services across the PCG so as to:

- develop and support primary and community healthcare provision;

- reduce variation in the provision of primary care services;

- improve the quality and standard of care provided to patients through the development of clinical governance; and

- integrate the delivery of primary and community health services.

Advising on, or commissioning directly, a range of hospital services for patients within their area that meets patients' needs appropriately by:

- commissioning effective and high-quality health services;

- monitoring the performance of providers of services against the service agreements; and

- contributing to the national drive to reduce waiting lists and times.

Source: Ref. 48

229. PCGs/LHGs are important for the district nursing service for three reasons:

- the focus on geographical populations and reducing health inequalities means that it should be possible to resolve some of the problems in matching resources to demand and running the service efficiently. These have occurred partly because of GP fundholding and partly due to variations in the quality of general practice. For example, some of the inflexibility caused by rigid practice attachment could be removed by the formation of larger groupings of GPs in PCGs/LHGs.

- all the main players should be involved locally in the PCG/LHG – with community nurses and social services represented alongside GPs; and

- the potential, with pooled budgets and lead commissioning arrangements, to dissolve barriers and co-ordinate health and social care services to deliver a better service to patients and carers.

230. There will be four stages of PCG development:

Stage 1   acts in an advisory capacity to support commissioning

Stage 2   is a health authority subcommittee with responsibility for managing devolved budgets for healthcare

Stage 3   becomes a free-standing PCT accountable for commissioning all primary and secondary care services within an integrated primary and secondary care budget

Stage 4   a PCT with added responsibilities for providing community health services

The changes set out in this report are radical and fundamental.

231. The majority of PCGs will start at Stage 1 or Stage 2 (all LHGs will start at Stage 1), depending largely on members' previous experience of GP fundholding, total purchasing project or GP commissioning group pilots. At Stage 2, PCGs will be responsible for devolved budgets, typically £70 million, from unified general medical service and hospital and community health service budgets. PCGs will be responsible for ensuring value for money in the use of these resources. It will not be possible for PCGs to move to Stage 3 or Stage 4 (PCT statu) until new legislation is passed. This is not expected until April 2000, but a significant minority of PCGs are then expected to become PCTs.

232. Community nurses, including district nurses, are expected to make a significant contribution to informing and shaping the decisions that PCGs/LHGs will need to make in carrying out these main functions. It will be important for community nurses to find their place as equals alongside other members of the PCG/LHG board. They are uniquely placed to contribute to the PCGs/LHGs work on health needs assessment and the tackling of variations in service provision.

233. The changes set out in this report are radical and fundamental. They will require changes in institutionalised relationships between GPs, community health and social services, the organisational development of the service and the development of individuals.

RECOMMENDATIONS

5   Moving Forward

In order to improve the quality and efficiency of district nursing, managers need to:

1   work with others to define the objectives and role of the service more clearly

2   agree with local social services and others how social care needs will be met and co-ordinated so that users receive care from the appropriate provider at the right time

3   influence and manage demand by improving the referral process

4   use systematic and regular caseload profiling to better align skills, resources and workloads with patients' needs

5   identify and tackle poor clinical performance and deficiencies in the dissemination of good practice by making better use of clinical nurse specialists, clinical audit and clinical supervision

6   review the numbers and mix of staff on duty against patient needs at different times

7   delegate clinical and non-patient-related activity to enable district nurses to fulfil their role in clinical and team management

8   review the need for, and provision of, district nursing services out of hours

9   extend the provision of clinic-based services on a planned basis

To manage district nursing more efficiently and effectively, trusts should:

10   consider introducing new forms of organisation that integrate district nurses with other community nurses

11   invest in professional development programmes for community nursing staff to support the development of self-managing teams

12   develop a performance management system for evaluating team performance on a regular basis

13   appoint team facilitator(s) to provide continuing support to teams

14   invest in leadership skills above and beyond the management role of team co-ordinator

Appendix 1

Membership of the Advisory Group

The study team is grateful for the guidance provided by the Advisory Group members:

Heather Ballard	Community and District Nursing Association (CDNA)
Jackie Carnell	Community Practitioners and Health Visitors Association (CPHVA)
Adrienne Fresko	Audit Commissioner
Tessa Harding	Help the Aged
Judy Hargadon	Chief Executive, Barnet Health Authority
Gail Jones	Palliative care nurse, Rochdale
Ros Lowe	Audit Commissioner
Dr David Lyon	Castlefields Health Centre, Runcorn
Alison Norman	Director of Nursing, North Staffordshire Combined NHS Trust and President, UKCC
Dr Geoff Roberts	Royal College of General Practitioners
Thelma Sackman	Department of Health (until April 1998)
Helena Shovelton	Audit Commissioner
Ginny Storey	Department of Health (from May 1998)
Sue Thomas	Royal College of Nursing (RCN)
Heather Wood	Nursing Officer, Welsh Office
David Woods	Director of Community Services, North Mersey Community NHS Trust then (from May 1998), Associate Dean for Education, School of Nursing, Midwifery and Health Visiting, University of Manchester.

Appendix 2

District Nursing Workforce

Nationally, figures on the numbers of district nurses are confused. Prior to 1995 data were recorded by area of work and grade. In England, the numbers working in district nursing fluctuated around 19,000 wte over the late 1980s and early 1990s, while those identified as 'district nurses' (but not necessarily qualified as such) reduced from 10,019 wte in 1990 to 8,570 in 1994.

But, in April 1995, the NHS introduced a new occupational coding system that separately identifies district nurses who occupy posts for which a district nursing qualification is required. Other registered nurses and unregistered nursing staff working in community nursing cannot be exclusively allocated to the district nursing service. As a result, it is no longer possible to distinguish how many registered nurses and unregistered nursing staff work in district nursing. Moreover, because of unreliable reporting, recent figures on the numbers of qualified district nurses in NHS employment are acknowledged to be inaccurate. For example, not all the data provided by trusts in the 1995 census had the appropriate pay scale and occupation codes. As a result, the number of 'district nurses' reported by some trusts in England doubled between 1995 and 1996, and no data for Wales were made available.

The non-medical workforce censuses for England and Wales report that there were 13,457 first-level district nurses in post at 30 September 1997 together with 2,279 second-level (or district-enrolled) nurses.[I] The figure for first-level district nurses accounts for three-quarters of those 17,909 individuals on the UKCC Register who have recorded a first-level district nursing qualification and who are resident in England or Wales.[II]

The Audit Commission's national survey of district nurses found that 70 per cent of those with a district nursing qualification were working as district nurses. Others were working in liaison or bank nurse posts (4 per cent), community staff nurse posts (3 per cent) and in NHS management (4 per cent). A further 2 per cent were working as GP practice nurses and 3 per cent as agency or independent sector nurses. Only one in eight was not currently working, or was employed in a non-nursing job.

The Audit Commission's survey of trusts identified 18,909 wte staff working in district nursing – excluding those working nights – of whom 6,603 wte were in posts at grade G or above, 8,909 wte in posts at grades C to F and 3,397 wte in post at grades A and B. Combining these figures, with the known 1997 number and wte figures for first-level qualified district nurses in England and Wales, we estimate that there are an additional 18,200 other registered nurses and 6,950 nursing auxiliaries working in district nursing.

I In order to practise, nurses must be registered with the United Kingdom Central Council for Nursing, Midwifery and Health Visiting (UKCC). A first-level registered nurse is a practitioner registered on Parts 1, 3, 5 or 8 to 15 of the Register. A second-level (or enrolled) nurse is a practitioner registered on Parts 2, 4, 6 or 7 of the Register. Training for entry to second-level parts of the Register (which was two years rather than three) was discontinued with the implementation of pre-registration diploma (Project 2000) education in the early 1990s.

II Note that, although district nursing is a specialist qualification which the UKCC considers appropriate to record against a practitioner's entry in the Register, there is no statutory requirement for individuals to record such qualifications. These statistics therefore represent only a count of those who have chosen to have the qualification recorded. A further 3,520 individuals have recorded a district enrolled nurse qualification. These data are not a precise guide to the numbers qualifying each year since practitioners can record qualifications achieved in earlier years. Note that the numbers recording district enrolled nurse qualifications have dropped to single figures, reflecting the ending of training for second level parts of the Register.

Appendix 3

Study Sites

Main study sites trusts

The study team visited seven NHS trusts (main study sites) to gather data on their district nursing services. These trusts were selected using a combination of data on district nursing costs (derived from the trust financial return – TFR2) and data on the population over 75 served by the trust (derived from survey data collected as part of the Audit Commission's study of information technology in the community). These data were used to identify a sample of 38 trusts with similar district nursing costs (a range of £216 to £300, at 1996 prices) per head of population over 75 (used as a crude proxy for demand). Other variables were explored to provide a mix of trusts with similar cost per head but with varying patterns of service delivery, numbers of patients seen, population and environmental characteristics. The variables used in this final selection included NHS region, number of patients seen, total contacts, trust type, ethnic minority population, geographic area covered, numbers of GP fundholders and proportion of contacts in clinics.

The main study sites were:

> Camden and Islington Community Health Services NHS Trust
>
> Community Healthcare Bolton NHS Trust
>
> Community Health Sheffield NHS Trust
>
> Clwydian Community Care NHS Trust
>
> North Kent NHS Trust (now part of Thames Gateway NHS Trust)
>
> Northumberland Community Health NHS Trust (now part of Northumbria Healthcare NHS Trust)
>
> Severn NHS Trust

At the week-long study site visits, data were collected by direct enquiry of the trusts' patient, personnel and financial information systems, by semi-structured interviews and group discussions, by shadowing district nurses and through documentation reviews. A number of data collection exercises were conducted in the fortnight following each site visit. These included practitioner diaries, caseload reviews, and prospective referral surveys. These exercises are described in Appendix 4.

We are grateful to the staff at all of these trusts for their help with data collection and for spending time talking to the team.

Other sites

In addition to the main study sites, short visits were made to a number of other NHS trusts and GP practices, either to help with the early development of the study or, subsequently, to investigate specific aspects of the service. These trusts and general practices were:

Brighton Healthcare NHS Trust

Bradford Community Health NHS Trust

Castlefields Health Centre (Runcorn)

Gwent Community Health NHS Trust

Nettleham Medical Practice (Lincoln)

North Mersey Community Health Services NHS Trust

North Staffordshire Combined Healthcare NHS Trust

Riverside Community Health NHS Trust

Southampton NHS Community Trust

West Berkshire Priority Care NHS Trust

West Lindsey NHS Trust

Thanks are due to the staff of these trusts and practices for the time that they spent with members of the team.

Appendix 4

Data Sources

National surveys

Two national surveys were conducted as part of this study. These were:

- a survey of all trusts providing district nursing services; and
- a national survey of district nurses.

Audit Commission survey of trusts

All trusts (187) which reported providing district nursing services in the 1996/97 Department of Health and Welsh Office District Nursing Statistics or TFR2 were given an eight-page proforma in November 1997 by their local audit manager.

The proforma requested data for 1996/97, and previous years, relating to:

- wte district nursing staff by grade
- management structures
- out-of-hours and weekend service provision and staffing
- Marie Curie night-sitting services
- wte numbers of specialist nursing staff by grade
- hospital-at-home and hospice-at-home schemes
- numbers of GPs, fundholding, non-fundholding and single-handed practices
- attachment of district nurses to GP practices
- wte numbers of district nursing staff working in integrated nursing teams
- district nursing first contacts by age group
- population age-profile in the trust's catchment area
- main purchasers and contract currencies
- clinical audits undertaken in the previous two years
- information systems used to record patient activity.

Overall, 171 completed questionnaires were returned: a simple response rate of 91 per cent. Telephone follow-up of the non-participants found that the majority had not completed the form because of anticipated mergers.

Audit Commission survey of district nurses

An eight-page questionnaire was sent to the home addresses of a random sample of 1,000 members of the RCN's District Nurse Forum and 500 members of the CDNA. The questionnaires were accompanied by a letter of endorsement from the General Secretary of the RCN and of the CDNA, as appropriate, and a reply-paid envelope. The questionnaire had previously been piloted with district nurses and with community staff nurses at one community trust.

The survey form was in four parts. These concerned:

- respondents' biographical details, qualifications and current employment;

- the management of district nursing teams;

- clinical supervision; and

- accessing evidence about clinical effectiveness.

The 15 per cent sample was selected at random from the RCN and CDNA membership records.[1] A reminder letter, a second copy of the questionnaire and a reply-paid envelope were sent to non-respondents after three weeks. By the close of the survey, 1,122 questionnaires were returned. This represents a simple response rate of 74.8 per cent. Excluding questionnaires returned as undeliverable by the post office, and those returned as inappropriate by the recipient, the useable response rate was 72 per cent.

The Audit Commission is grateful to both the RCN and the CDNA for their help with the organisation of the survey.

Patients' and carers' experiences

A qualitative study of patients' and carers' experiences of district nursing services was undertaken in the catchment areas of two NHS trusts. One trust covered part of inner London and the other included a mixed urban and rural area in south-east England. Ethical approval was obtained from the relevant ethics committees and a pilot study was undertaken with patients at a practice in south London.

The study focused on patients (and carers) who were receiving care for the probe conditions of continence or leg ulceration. Forty patients (20 from each of the target conditions) and 10 carers were selected at random from the different geographical areas and age bands. Caseload-holders were asked to exclude unsuitable patients. The main exclusion criteria were dementia, severe mental illness, advanced terminal illness and recent bereavement.

A semi-structured interview schedule based on Flanagan's critical incident technique (Ref. 49) was used and all interviews were tape-recorded and transcribed. Incidents and associated meanings were analysed using *Atlas ti* software.

The study was undertaken by Jenny Bartholomew and Adrienne Shaw from the Department of General Practice and Primary Care, Guy's King's and St Thomas's Medical School of King's College, London, under the advice of Dr Nicky Britten. Professor Fiona Ross advised on development of the interview schedule.

1   The District Nurses Forum had 9,083 members at the time of sampling. Membership of the Forum is open to all RCN members and there is no membership fee. The membership includes newly qualified nurses and pre-registration students who pay reduced RCN membership fees. These, together with members living outside England and Wales, were excluded from the population frame as they were unlikely to be working as district nurses. The sample of 1,000 was selected from an eligible population of 6,825. The CDNA sample was selected from members living in England and Wales, excluding any members who were not registered nurses.

Data Collection at Audit Commission s Study Sites

At each trust, the following primary data collection exercises were conducted:

Prospective referral survey

The aim of this exercise was to find out about the nature of the referrals, the quality of referral information and the perceived appropriateness of the referral. All district nursing teams were asked to record details of new referrals over a two week period. Referrals that did not lead to an identified patient contact (eg, large volume, one-off referrals for flu vaccinations or venepuncture) were excluded.

3,431 completed referral forms were returned by the seven trusts. Where response rates have been calculated (by comparing the number of referral forms completed with the number of first contacts recorded), these returns account for between 62 per cent and 82 per cent of first contacts in the same period.

Discharge liaison nurse survey

The aim of this exercise was to map the types of activities undertaken when organising a patient's discharge, the proportion of patients referred to district nursing services, and the time lapse between referral to the liaison nurse and discharge from hospital. Liaison nurses at four study site trusts were asked to record the details of each patient whose discharge they organised over a one-week period.

Nine liaison nurses completed 329 liaison discharge forms. Independent verification that this accounts for all patients dealt with by liaison nurses in this period is not possible because liaison nurse contacts are not systematically recorded by all trusts.

Review of assessment documentation

At each site, the assessment documentation for a random sample of 25 patients with continence problems and 25 patients with a leg ulcer(s) was requested. The assessments should have been conducted in the year beginning April 1997 and included patients seen in clinic as well as at home.

A total of 163 leg ulcer and 158 continence assessments were reviewed. The assessments were anonymised before the review was undertaken by an independent registered nurse. Patients were excluded if the documentation provided was a reassessment, a care plan or an evaluation sheet rather than the initial assessment.

Activity diary

At each trust, all nursing staff in district nursing teams (ie, district nurses, community staff nurses, enrolled nurses, nursing auxiliaries and healthcare assistants, Project 2000 diploma and nursing degree students on placement, district nurse students, temporary – bank or agency – nurses) were asked to complete a seven-day activity diary. Staff working out of hours and at weekends were included. The diary records the total time spent in a working day across six broad categories of activity (patient care, patient management, administration, teaching and learning, travel, other), shift start-times, contracted hours and any non-attendance.

The total number of diaries returned was 1,614. Accurate response rates are difficult to calculate for the diary exercise because of the inclusion of temporary staff and students. The overall response rate is estimated at 67 per cent, ranging from 64 per cent to 74 per cent of the known staff in post.

Caseload review

At each site, three general practices were selected using simple criteria (eg, single-handed, fundholding, non-fundholding, rural or urban location). The district nursing caseholders attached to each of these practices were asked to review their active (ie, only patients seen in the last six months) caseload. Note that in several cases these caseloads included patients from more than one practice who were being served by the same district nursing team.

In total, 21 caseloads were reviewed by the 25 district nurses (including four job shares) who had 24-hour continuing responsibility for patient care. A total of 2,168 patients from 39 practices were reviewed.

Other data sources

Published and unpublished data from a number of sources were obtained and used in the study.

- The UKCC provided unpublished data from the Professional Register on the numbers, and ages, of individuals who had recorded a district nursing or district-enrolled nursing qualification;

- The Office of Manpower Economics provided anonymised data for 248 trusts in England and Wales from the March 1997 Manpower Survey. These data related to wte numbers of first- and second-level district nurses in post, numbers of joiners and leavers over the previous 12 months, the number and duration of vacancies;

- The NHS Executive provided unpublished data for each NHS trust in England from the Non-medical Workforce Census, on the number and wte of first- and second-level district nurses in post at 30th September 1995, 1996 and 1997. Age profile data were also provided. The NHS Executive also provided data from the March 1996 and 1997 Financial and Workforce Information Return on the numbers of district nurse training places commissioned, forecast numbers of district nurses in post and forecast demand for newly qualified district nurses;

- The Welsh Office provided data by trust on the number and wte of first and second level district nurses in post at 30 September 1997. Age profile data were also provided;

- Health authorities which were the principal purchasers of services at four of the trusts provided data on wte numbers of practice nurses by practice and practice list size by age group;

- Published and unpublished data on intakes to district nurse training, in-training populations and numbers qualifying were provided by the English and Welsh National Boards.

Appendix 5

Hospital-at-home

'Hospital-at-home' is a generic term referring to home-based nursing and rehabilitation services which provide care that is usually available only in hospital. The two types of scheme are:

- admission avoidance schemes – referrals taken from GPs and district nurses of patients whom they would otherwise refer to hospital; and

- early discharge schemes – patients who are discharged early from hospital after elective or emergency admissions, to be cared for at home.

Thirty per cent of trusts in the Audit Commission's national survey had either an early discharge scheme (29 per cent), an admission prevention scheme (35 per cent), or both. They may be managed either by hospital trusts (out-reach schemes) or, more commonly, by community trusts (in-reach schemes). Some schemes deal only with particular specialties, notably orthopaedics or paediatrics.

With considerable pressure on hospital beds and high costs associated with acute hospital care, a major aim of hospital-at-home is to ensure that hospital resources are targeted at patients who cannot be managed in the community. In practice, however, some studies have found that hospital-at-home schemes are an additional, rather than substitute, service, with longer total length of stay for similar patients (Ref. 50).

The development of hospital-at-home schemes are relevant to this study because the nursing input is likely to be provided by district nursing staff. This is not always the case, however. At one site, hospital-at-home was co-ordinated by a district nurse but staffed by nurses recruited from the local acute hospital into F grade posts. In other instances, district nurses have been said to be reluctant to take on the extra work demanded by hospital-at-home.

Hospital-at-home schemes are commonly funded for a fixed-term period from special budgets (for example, LIZ monies in London) and health authorities then have to decide whether to continue funding from mainstream budgets.

Hospital-at-home has been promoted as a potential way to improve quality of care and to reduce costs. But few published evaluations exist, and those which do have been small, have used inconsistent outcome measures and have made little attempt at judging cost-effectiveness. Recent economic evaluations of schemes in Bristol and Northamptonshire have reached opposing conclusions. Frenchay Healthcare NHS Trust found reduced costs (mean cost to the NHS of £2,516 per hospital-at-home patient and £3,292 per hospital patient), despite greater length of stay (Ref. 51). In contrast, the Rockingham Forest NHS Trust study (Ref. 52) found that the overall duration of an episode was longer, that costs were higher for some patient groups, and that the proportion of patients who were eligible was low. These findings led the authors to conclude that hospital-at-home provided extra care in the community but not necessarily care that would otherwise have been provided in hospital. Elective surgery patients who are discharged early go home when their hospital care is least expensive. For elderly medical patients, hospital-at-home is unlikely to be cheaper because the relatively high nursing costs still have to be incurred (Ref. 53).

The Primary Care Support Force identifies ten critical factors for ensuring that hospital-at-home schemes are effective (Ref. 54). These schemes need:

- clear entry and exit requirements to ensure that admission is made available only to patients who would otherwise have required hospitalisation;

- consultant specialists and their hospital colleagues to understand and be involved in the initiative;

- everyone to understand how they can benefit from the scheme;

- a sufficient volume of activity;

- to focus on patient education and self-help;

- social care needs to be recognised and not considered a block;

- instant and sufficient access to specialist equipment;

- provision of 24-hour access to care;

- clear clinical accountability, protocols and explicit working agreements; and

- to incorporate the right to re-admit to a hospital bed immediately.

References

1. M Stocks, *A Hundred Years of District Nursing*, Allen & Unwin, London, 1960.

2. M C Stern, C Jagger, M Clarke, J Anderson, C McGrother, T Battock and C McDonald, 'Residential Care for Elderly People: A Decade of Change', *British Medical Journal*, Vol. 306, 1993, pp827-30.

3. G Barrett and M Hudson, 'Changes in District Nursing Workload', *Journal of Community Nursing*, Vol. 11, No. 3, 1997, pp4-8.

4. J Koffman and C Citrone, *Survey of District Nursing Service in Riverside Community Health Care NHS Trust: 13 February 1996* (unpublished report).

5. J Dexter and C Todd, *Community Health Sheffield: District Nursing Caseloads 1993-1995*, Sheffield Centre for Health and Related Research, 1996.

6. Department of Health and Social Security, *Neighbourhood Nursing: A Focus for Care, Report of the Community Nursing Review* (The Cumberlege Report), HMSO, London, 1986.

7. K Atkin and N Lunt, *Nurses in Practice: The Role of the Practice Nurse in Primary Health Care*, Social Policy Research Unit, University of York, 1995.

8. M Hirst, N Lunt and K Atkin, 'Were Practice Nurses Distributed Equitably Across England and Wales, 1988-1995?', *Journal of Health Services Research and Policy*, Vol. 3, No. 1, 1998, pp31-8.

9. Review Body for Nursing Staff, Midwives, Health Visitors and Professions Allied to Medicine, *Fifteenth Report on Nursing Staff, Midwives and Health Visitors*, The Stationery Office, 1998.

10. Department of Health, *The new NHS – Modern and Dependable*, The Stationery Office, 1997.

11. J Townsend, A O Frank, D Fermont, S Dyer, O Karran and A Walgrove, 'Terminal Cancer Care and Patients' Preference for Place of Death: A Prospective Study', *British Medical Journal*, Vol. 301, 1990, pp415-17.

12. Welsh Office, *NHS Wales – Putting Patients First*, The Stationery Office, 1998.

13. Department of Health, *Partnership in Action: New Opportunities for Joint Working between Health and Social Services*, Department of Health, 1998.

14. Welsh Office, *Partnership for Improvement: New Opportunities for Joint Working between Health and Local Authorities in Wales*, Welsh Office, 1998.

15. Audit Commission, *Goods for Your Health: Improving Supplies Management in NHS Trusts*, Audit Commission, 1996.

16. Audit Commission, *Comparing Notes: A Study of Information Management in Community Trusts*, Audit Commission, 1997.

17. A Worth, J McIntosh, O Carney and J Lugton, *Assessment of Need for District Nursing*, Department of Nursing & Community Health, Glasgow Caledonian University, Research Monograph No. 1, 1995.

18. C Glendinning, K Rummery and R Clarke, 'From Collaboration to Commissioning: Developing Relationships between Primary Health and Social Services', *British Medical Journal*, Vol. 317, 11 July 1998, pp122-5.

19. Audit Commission, *Coming of Age: Improving Care Services for Older People*, Audit Commission, 1997.

20. A Worth, A Tierney, M Macmillan, C King and F Atkinson, *A National Survey of Community Nursing Staff's Experience and Views Relating to Discharge of Elderly People Following Acute Hospital Care*, Department of Nursing Studies, University of Edinburgh, 1993.

21. R Savill and J Bartholomew, 'Planning Better Discharges', *Journal of Community Nursing*, Vol. 8, No. 3, 1994, pp10-14.

22. M A Anderson and L B Hems, 'Communication between Continuing Care Organisations', *Research in Nursing and Health*, No. 18, 1995, pp49-57.

23. A Timmins, *Dilemmas of Discharge: The Case of District Nursing*, Department of Nursing and Midwifery Studies, University of Nottingham, 1996.

24. L Freak, D Simon, J Walsh, C Lane, A Kinsella, C McCollum, J Walsh and C Lane, 'Leg Ulcer Care in the UK: An Audit of Cost-Effectiveness', *Health Trends*, Vol. 27, No. 4, 1995, pp133-6.

25. Royal College of Physicians, *Incontinence: Causes, Management and Provision of Services*, Royal College of Physicians, 1995.

26. CEST, *Advanced Medical Textiles*, CEST, London, 1991.

27. NHS Centre for Reviews and Dissemination, 'Compression Therapy for Venous Leg Ulcers', *Effective Health Care Bulletin*, Vol. 3, No. 4, 1997.

28. RCN Institute, Centre of Evidence-Based Nursing, University of York, and the School of Nursing, Midwifery and Health Visiting, University of Manchester, *Clinical Practice Guidelines for the Management of Patients with Venous Leg Ulcers*, RCN Institute, Centre of Evidence-Based Nursing, University of York, and the School of Nursing, Midwifery and Health Visiting, University of Manchester, 1998.

29. Royal College of Physicians, *Promoting Continence: Clinical Audit Scheme for the Management of Urinary and Faecal Incontinence*, Research Unit, Royal College of Physicians, 1998.

30. Audit Commission, *Home Alone: The Role of Housing in Community Care*, Audit Commission, 1997.

31. P McDonald, 'Can Timed Appointments for Community Staff Improve Care?' *Nursing Times*, Vol. 92, No. 18, 1996, pp35-7.

32. Department of Health, *The Patient's Charter*, Department of Health, 1995.

33. M Avis, 'Incorporating Patients' Voices in the Audit Process', *Quality in Health Care*, Vol. 6, 1997, pp86-91.

34. R Carr-Hill, 'The Measurement of Patient Satisfaction', *Journal of Public Health Medicine*, Vol. 14, No. 3, 1992, pp236-49.

35. B Williams, 'Patient Satisfaction: A Valid Concept?' *Social Science and Medicine*, Vol. 38, No.4, 1994, pp509-16.

36. UKCC, *Position Statement on Clinical Supervision for Nursing and Health Visiting*, UKCC, 1996.

37. J Griffiths and K Luker, 'A Barrier to Clinical Effectiveness: The Etiquette of District Nursing', *Journal of Clinical Effectiveness in Nursing*, Vol. 1, 1997, pp121-30.

38. K Luker and M Kenrick, 'Towards Knowledge-Based Practice: An Evaluation of A Method of Dissemination', *International Journal of Nursing Studies*, Vol. 32, No. 1, 1995, pp49-67.

39. NHS Centre for Reviews and Dissemination, 'Implementing Clinical Practice Guidelines', *Effective Health Care Bulletin*, Vol. 1, No. 8, 1994.

40. J Morrell, *Cost-effectiveness of Community Leg Ulcer Clinics: Guidance for Purchasers and Providers*, School of Health and Related Research, University of Sheffield, 1997.

41. I Higginson, B Jarman, P Astin and S Dolan, 'Do Social Factors Affect Where Patients Die: An Analysis of 10 Years of Cancer Deaths in England', *Journal of Public Health Medicine* (to be published this year).

42. HVA, *Integrated Nursing Team – Initial Information: Professional Briefing 1*, HVA, 1996.

43. K Gerrish, *An Evaluation of Integrated Nursing Teams in Sheffield* (unpublished report submitted to Community Health Sheffield NHS Trust), Sheffield Hallam University, 1997.

44. J Bull, 'Integrated Nursing: A Review of the Literature', *British Journal of Community Nursing*, Vol. 3, No. 3, 1998, pp124-9.

45. E Godfrey, P Rink and F Ross, 'Measuring the Workload of An Integrated Nursing Team in General Practice,' *British Journal of Community Nursing*, Vol. 2, No. 7, 1997, pp350-5.

46. Department of Health, *Caring for People: Community Care in the Next Decade and Beyond*, HMSO, 1989.

47. A Bergen, 'The Role of Community Nurses as Care Managers', *British Journal of Community Health Nursing*, Vol. 2, No. 10, 1995, pp466-73.

48. NHS Executive, *The new NHS Modern and Dependable: Developing Primary Care Groups*, Department of Health, 1998 (HSC 1998/139).

49. I Norman, S Redfern, D Tomalin and S Oliver, 'Developing Flanagan's Critical Incident Technique to Elicit Indicators of High and Low Quality Nursing Care from Patients and their Nurses', *Journal of Advanced Nursing*, Vol. 17, 1992, pp590-600.

50. N Fulop, S Hood and S Parsons, 'Does the National Health Service Want Hospital at Home?' *Journal of Royal Society of Medicine*, Vol. 90, 1997, pp211-15.

51. J Coast, S Richards, T Peters, D Gunnell, M A Marlow and J Pounsford, 'Hospital at Home or Acute Hospital Care?: A Cost Minimisation Analysis', *British Medical Journal*, Vol. 316, 1998, pp1802-6.

52. S Shepperd, D Harwood, C Jenkinson, A Gray, M Vessey and P Morgan, 'Randomised Controlled Trial Comparing Hospital at Home Care with In-patient Hospital Care (I): A Three Month Follow-up of Health Outcomes', *British Medical Journal*, Vol. 316, 1998, pp1786-91.

53. S Shepperd, D Harwood, A Gray, M Vessey and P Morgan, 'Randomised Controlled Trial Comparing Hospital at Home Care with In-Patient Hospital Care (II): A Cost Minimisation Analysis', *British Medical Journal*, Vol. 316, 1998, pp1791-6.

54. Primary Care Support Force, *Ten Critical Factors for Achieving Effective Hospital at Home*, Primary Care Support Force, 1997.

Glossary

Assessment

The process of gathering and evaluating information about the patient's health, home and personal circumstances on admission to the caseload in order that nursing needs can be identified and a holistic nursing care plan formulated. The assessment is usually recorded on a standardised pre-printed form, retained as part of the patient-held record. There may be separate forms for short- and long-term patients and for specific care packages (for example, continence care).

Attachment

An attached district nursing team is one that spends the majority of its time caring for the patients on the list of a particular GP(s) or practice(s). They may or may not be based in the practice premises.

Auxiliary

An unregistered nurse working as part of the district nursing team under the supervision of a registered nurse.

Bank nurse

A nurse supplied to a district nursing team on a temporary basis from a list maintained by the trust, the directorate or the locality.

Care plan

Plan of nursing care for an individual patient based on the problems identified during the assessment and drawn up in consultation with the patient and carers. Progress should be evaluated against the goals on review dates specified in the plan.

Caseholder

District nurse with continuing responsibility for patients on the caseload.

Caseload

Number of patients for whom the district nursing team provides care, irrespective of the practice with which they are registered or the frequency with which they are seen. May be subdivided into active or inactive (the former usually being patients who have been seen within a defined period).

Casemix

Profile of patients on the caseload grouped in a clinically meaningful way.

Clinical audit

A clinically led initiative that seeks to improve the quality and outcome of patient care through structured peer review, whereby clinicians examine their practices and results against explicit standards and modify their practice where indicated.

Clinical effectiveness

The extent to which specific clinical interventions achieve their intended outcomes (that is, secure the largest possible health gain from the available resources).

Clinical governance

Initiative designed to assure and improve clinical standards at local level throughout the NHS. Includes action to ensure that risks are avoided, that adverse events are rapidly detected, openly investigated and lessons learned, that good practice is rapidly disseminated and that systems are in place to ensure continuous improvements in clinical care.

Clinical guidelines	Systematically developed statements that assist clinicians and patients in making decisions about appropriate and effective treatment for specific conditions.
Clinical nurse specialists	Clinical nurse specialists are experts (usually with advanced education) in a particular clinical area or have expertise about the needs of a specific client group.
Clinical supervision	A process through which skilled supervisors can help practitioners to reflect on their clinical practice.
Contact	A contact is any face-to-face meeting between a member of the district nursing team and an individual patient or patient's proxy, where treatment or advice is given and the location is anywhere other than a hospital ward or outpatient clinic. Where a patient is seen by more than one nurse at the same time, only one contact is recorded.
First contact	A first contact is the first time that a patient is seen in the financial year by a district nurse. A subsequent contact with a different nurse employed by the same service provider does not count as a first contact, so each patient is recorded only once in any year by any trust. This is a measure of the number of people who receive care during the year.
Health improvement programme (HImP)	The local strategy for improving health and healthcare. The health authority will have lead responsibility for drawing up the strategy in consultation with NHS trusts, PCGs/LHGs, other primary care professionals such as dentists, opticians and pharmacists, the public and other agencies. The HImP will cover the health needs and healthcare requirements of the local population and how these are to be met by the NHS and/or partner organisations.
Initial contact	An initial contact is the first in an episode of care with a service-provider. An episode of care may be initiated by a referral to the district nursing service from a hospital, GP or other health service professional. Where a previous episode of care for the same patient did not end with a positive discharge from care, a new episode is recorded only if more than six months have elapsed since the last contact. This is a measure of the number of new episodes of care commenced in the year.
Integrated nursing team	A team of community-based nurses from different disciplines, working together in a primary care setting in order to provide the most effective care for patients within the community or practice that it covers. Teams may include district nurses, practice nurses, health visitors, community psychiatric nurses and school nurses.
Liaison nurse	Nurse responsible for liaising between hospital and community services about arrangements for the continuing care of patients on discharge from hospital.
Link nurse	A registered nurse who provides a link between a clinical nurse specialist and members of the district nursing team for a particular package of care. The role of the link nurse varies, but will include cascading information.

Local health group (LHG)	New groups bringing together family doctors and community nurses in Wales to contribute to the local HImP.
Locality	For administrative and management purposes, most community trusts subdivide the area over which they provide services into discrete geographical localities.
Out of hours	Nursing services provided in the early morning, in the evening or at night which are outside the 'normal' working day as defined locally.
On-call	Day staff 'on-call' for duties outside their normal daytime working hours.
Practice nurse	A registered nurse employed by a general practitioner.
Primary care group (PCG)	New groups bringing together family doctors and community nurses in England to contribute to the local HImP.
Primary care trust (PCT)	A PCG which is accountable to the Health Authority for commissioning care, and with added responsibility for the providing community services for its population.
Protocol	A document prescribing the sequence of steps to be followed in undertaking a particular nursing activity.
Rapid response team	Multidisciplinary team providing an extension to the district nursing service for more heavily dependent patients who would otherwise require hospitalisation.
Standards of care	Authoritative statements of (a) minimum levels of acceptable performance or results, or (b) excellent levels of performance or results, or (c) the range of acceptable performance or results.
Whole-time-equivalent (wte)	Term used to describe calculations that express the hours of part-time employees as a proportion of a full-time post (37.5 hours).

Notes

1. A recent survey asked 5,000 carers to indicate which NHS staff had the most power to improve their life as a carer, which had been most effective in providing them with help and information, and which had given the most practical support. Respondents identified district/community nurses as second, after GPs, in their ability to make a difference to the lives of carers and in providing help and information. They were also ranked alongside GPs as the most important staff in giving practical support (M Henwood, *Ignored and Invisible? Carer's Experience of the NHS*, Carers National Association, 1998).

2. The full patient contact figures by age and gender for 1997/98 (England) are as follows:

Age at first contact in the year	Number of first contacts in the year (000s)		
	Total	**Males**	**Females**
Under 5	34.2	19.5	14.7
5-15	64.4	35.3	29.1
16-24	94.0	42.5	51.5
25-34	160.4	63.9	96.5
35-44	167.4	68.4	98.9
45-54	216.8	92.3	124.5
55-64	274.4	128.3	146.1
65-74	470.8	207.0	263.8
75-84	688.6	241.0	447.6
85 and over	458.5	115.4	343.1
Total	**2,629.4**	**1,013.5**	**1,615.9**

Source: *Patient Care in the Community: District Nursing – Summary Information for 1997/98, England, Department of Health, 1998.*

Data for Wales are reported in different age bands. These show that the district nursing patient profile is older. In 1996/97, 68 per cent of patients were aged 65 or over (*source: Health Statistics Wales 1997, Welsh Office, 1998*).

3. In 1997/98 there were 2.63 million first contacts in England (*source: Patient Care in the Community: District Nursing – Summary Information for 1997/98, England, Department of Health, 1998*). In Wales the latest figures are for 1996/97. These show 159,000 first contacts (*source: Health Statistics Wales 1997, Welsh Office, 1998*).

4. The Cumberlege report recommended that each district health authority should identify neighbourhoods (with populations of between 10,000 and 25,000) for the purposes of planning, organising and providing nursing and related primary care services.

5. This figure comes from the Audit Commission's survey of trusts. Ten per cent of district nursing staff are not GP-attached. These are mainly dedicated evening and night service staff, who tend to work geographically, and nursing auxiliaries who, in some trusts, work for different teams across a geographical area in response to changing workloads. In more than half of the trusts that responded, all district nursing staff are attached to GP practices.

6. This is a crude exercise, not least because demand for district nursing depends on far more than simple population size. For example, a small practice with a large elderly population may have a bigger district nursing team than a practice with a larger list size but younger age profile.

7. Practice nurse numbers rose from 2,768 wte in 1987 to 10,080 wte in 1997 (source: *Bi-annual Census of General Medical Practitioners*, Department of Health, 1997).

8. The exercise has several limitations:
    *   practice nurses treat many patients who would not traditionally have anything to do with district nurses;
    *   the resource 'allocated' to the practice may not be the resource available due to staff absence or vacancies;
    *   population size is not necessarily a good indicator of need;
    *   the exercise does not take account of grade-mix; and
    *   in some integrated nursing teams, health visitors may also take on a similar caseload to district nurses and practice nurses.

9. In the year to the end of March 1997, there were 495 (wte) leavers from posts requiring a district nursing qualification in England and Wales. This was equivalent to 8.5 per cent of the staff-in-post. The comparable figures for other first-level nursing staff groups were: 10.3 per cent for health visitors and 13 per cent for other first-level-registered nurses. Figures are derived from unpublished data on 248 trusts provided by the Office of Manpower Economics from its Manpower Survey, 1997. Vacancy data are derived from the same source. This shows that at 31 March 1997, 2.1 per cent of posts requiring a district nursing qualification were vacant. This compares with figures of 2.7 per cent in health visiting, 2.6 per cent in other community nursing posts and 5.6 per cent in mental illness.

10. Ageing of the workforce is even more marked among nursing auxiliaries – one in three are aged 50 or over, with one in seven aged 55 or over. At one study site trust, more than one-third of nursing auxiliaries were aged over 55. It is likely that the high level of retirements of auxiliaries will mean that much of the effort to increase the number of healthcare assistants will be put into replacing them rather than facilitating skill substitution within the district nursing workforce.

11. In the late 1980s, almost one thousand nurses started district nurse training in England and Wales each year. In 1997/98, just 605 did so (*source: ENB Annual Report 1997/98, English National Board, 1998*, and unpublished figures provided by the Welsh National Board). As a consequence, the number of people recording district nursing qualifications on the UKCC Register has also been declining, until very recently. The number of district nursing qualifications being recorded on the Register (for England and Wales) has more than halved, falling from 952 in 1987/88 to 452 in 1997/98 (source: unpublished figures provided by the UKCC).

12. Source: unpublished data from the March 1998 Financial and Workforce Information Return provided by the NHS Executive. These show the number of district nurses (first-level) in post (England) in 1997/98 at 9,881 wte rising to 10,108 in 2001/02, and the demand for newly qualified district nurses falling from 498 in 1998/99 to 455 in 2001/02.

13. Block contracts are those where the purchaser pays an annual sum in instalments in return for a defined range of services with limited volume specification. They may be 'simple' or 'complex'. Simple contracts do not vary with the level of activity; complex contracts adjust price when activity breaches set thresholds.

14. Where a patient is seen by more than one nurse at a time only one contact is recorded.

15. In 1996 the Department of Health started collecting data on contact 'intensity', distinguishing contacts in excess of 30 minutes, and 'assisted visits' (that is, those involving more than one nurse). These data are reported at health authority, rather than trust, level. Over the ten quarters available, the proportion of visits of more than 30 minutes has fluctuated between 28 and 29 per cent, while the proportion of visits involving more than one nurse shows a downward trend from 5.4 per cent in the first quarter of 1996/97 to 4.9 per cent in the second quarter of 1998/99. The consultation document on the new framework for assessing performance (NHS Executive, *The new NHS – Modern and Dependable: A National Framework for Assessing Performance*, Department of Health, 1998) proposed, as a measure of access to community services, a composite indicator that consists of:

    • district nurse, and assisted district nurse, contacts for those aged 75 and over; and

    • district nurse contacts over 30 minutes for those aged 75 and over.

16. A pressure sore care package, for example, would include provision of nursing care to patients with, or at risk of, pressure sores, covering: assessment; wound management/treatment for pressure sores; health promotion; monitoring or support of patient or carer; liaison with other health professionals; and teaching patients or carers.

17. These referrals will not always result in continuing district nursing care. District nurses did not intend to re-visit one in four of these patients after the initial assessment.

18. In a survey of 5,000 carers, the Carers National Association found that more than half of those who had not had visits, help or advice from a district nurse believed that they would have found it helpful (M Henwood, *Ignored and Invisible? Carer's Experience of the NHS*, Carers National Association, 1998).

19. A hospital-at-home scheme was introduced by one study site in 1992 for elderly people who had been discharged from medical wards. The scheme had three aims:

    • to enable earlier discharge than would conventionally be the case;

    • to provide intensive domiciliary rehabilitation of up to four weeks; and

    • to provide support and training to carers.

    The hospital-at-home team included a nurse manager, physiotherapist, occupational therapist and three part-time support workers. Nursing care was provided by the local district nurses. A randomised controlled trial found that, while patients allocated to hospital-at-home were discharged on average five days earlier, improvements in independence were modest (I Donald, R N Baldwin and M Bananerjee, 'Gloucester Hospital at Home: A Randomised Controlled Trial', *Age and Ageing*, Vol. 24, 1995, pp 434-9). Overall, the net extra costs of hospital-at-home were estimated at £177 per patient. The health authority withdrew funding in April 1998 on the grounds that the scheme was not cost-effective.

20. These examples, which have not been independently evaluated, were provided by the NHS Executive.

21. On average, trusts have 13,450 initial contacts per year. This estimate assumes that each inappropriate referral takes an hour of G grade time and that, on average, 10 per cent – or 1,345 hours of G grade time at the mid-point of the scale (plus employers on-costs) – would cost £22,030.

22. Nearly two-thirds of trusts with a district nursing service now employ a liaison nurse, usually in G or H grade posts. Most trusts have one or two wte liaison nurses while a few have committed considerable resources to liaison: one trust had 8.5 wte liaison nurses at G grade and 0.5 wte at H grade, a salary cost alone of approximately £187,760.

23. The number of 'active' patients (those seen in the last six months) on these caseloads ranged from 23 to 268. Actual caseloads may be larger than this. At some study sites, district nurses did not 'discharge' patients from the IT system despite not seeing the patient for six months. At one site, only half the patients who were identified on the patient information system as part of the district nursing caseload had actually been seen by a member of the district nursing team in the previous six months. Other trusts automatically 'discharge' patients from the caseload if the information system shows that the patient had not been seen within a defined period.

24. The West Lindsey patient dependency tool was developed in an attempt to explain the differences in time spent by district nurses on patients with the same diagnosis. The tool measures dependency of the patient on the district nursing team rather than the patient's dependency per se (that is, his/her dependency on carers and/or social services). It is not intended as a description of the patient. The tool is composed of 11 variables that reflect most of the nursing care required to support and maintain a patient in their home. Some aspects of daily living activities and mental health status are deliberately omitted because other tools are available that can be used alongside the West Lindsey tool. Each of the variables is scored from one to five. These categories are not meant to be evenly weighted; however, category one is considered to be less severe than category five. The tool allows for subjectivity when categorising the degree of dependency for each variable (W Coffey, *The Evaluation of a Tool to Measure Patient Nurse Dependency in the Community*, unpublished dissertation submitted for MSc Applied Research and Quality Evaluation, University of Sheffield, 1997). The dependency tool has been validated and used by district nurses in West Lindsey NHS Trust since 1993. District nurses have used it to monitor patients' dependency on the district nursing service over time and to demonstrate when patients have been inappropriately discharged to residential homes instead of to nursing homes.

25. One-quarter of these non-dependent patients were visited monthly. Visits to such patients may, of course, be important (for example, in providing preventative care or in giving carers confidence to cope with a reduced nursing input).

26. For example, research has suggested that patients living on their own, and women patients with a male carer, are more likely to continue receiving district nursing care than patients with informal carers or male patients with a woman carer (K Luker and E Perkins, 'The Elderly at Home: Service Needs and Provision', *Journal of the Royal College of General Practitioners*, Vol. 37, 1987, pp248-50).

27. Other estimates are much higher. For example, Douglas and Simpson estimated the cost to the NHS in 1995 at £600 million (W S Douglas and N B Simpson, 'Guidelines for the Management of Chronic Venous Leg Ulceration: Report of A Multi-disciplinary Workshop', *British Journal of Dermatology*, Vol. 132, 1995, pp446-52).

28. Routine investigations, including blood pressure measurement (to monitor arterial disease), weight (to monitor weight loss if the patient is obese) and routine urine tests (to screen for undiagnosed diabetes mellitus), should be recorded at the initial assessment. These investigations can reveal a variety of conditions that may predispose the patient to ulceration or affect their rate of healing. Recent clinical audit at study sites shows that these clinical investigations are not carried out routinely. A review of documentation by the tissue viability nurse at one study site found that blood pressure was not recorded on 71 per cent (27 out of 38) of patient assessments and that there was no urine test on 66 per cent

(25/38). In another study site, a clinical audit in 1996 showed that blood pressure was not recorded on 32 per cent (13 out of 41) of assessments, no blood screening tests on 66 per cent (27/41) and no urine test on 34 per cent (14/41).

29. Doppler ultrasound readings should be taken only as part of a comprehensive assessment of the patient as a number of clinical factors (for example, oedema, diabetes, rheumatoid arthritis, obesity, renal disease) as well as poor technique or miscalculation by the practitioner, can give false high readings. Evidence suggests that, unless operators have undergone formal training in Doppler ultrasound technique, the ABPI measurement can be unreliable (C M Fisher, A Burnett, V Makeham, J Kidd, M Glasson and J P Harris, 'Variation in Measurement of ABPI Pressure Index in Routine Clinical Practice', *Journal of Vascular Surgery*, Vol. 24, 1996, pp871-5). In some trusts, nurses must be authorised by their manager to undertake Doppler ultrasound and there are a set of criteria in place to judge whether that authorisation should be given. In one study site, the tissue viability nurse has recommended the withdrawal of Doppler probes until all potential users are competent in their use. One audit (J Stevens, P J Franks and M Harrington, 'A Community/Hospital Leg Ulcer Service', *Journal of Wound Care*, Vol. 6, No. 2, 1997, pp62-8) found that over 80 per cent of leg ulcer patients known to a district nursing service had not been assessed using Doppler ultrasound. In another study (E Elliot, B Russell and G Jaffrey, 'Setting a Standard for Leg Ulcer Assessment', *Journal of Wound Care*, Vol. 5, No. 4, 1996, pp173-5) half of the district nurses used visual assessment alone to determine ulcer type.

30. A significant proportion of patients with venous leg ulcers report moderate to severe pain, which may result from the ulcer, the dressing and/or the treatment (C Walshe, 'Living with a Venous Leg Ulcer: A Descriptive Study of Patients' Experiences', *Journal of Advanced Nursing*, Vol. 22, 1995, pp1092-100). In a study of patients' perceptions of chronic leg ulceration, 35 per cent reported that pain was the worst thing about having a leg ulcer (C Hamer, N Cullum and B H Roe, 'Patients' Perceptions of Chronic Leg Ulcers', *Journal of Wound Care*, Vol. 3, 1994, pp99-101). One survey (B H Roe, K A Luker, N A Cullum, J M Griffiths and M Kenrick, 'Assessment, Prevention and Monitoring of Chronic Leg Ulcers in the Community: A Report of A Survey', *Journal of Clinical Nursing*, Vol. 2, 1993, pp299-306) found that over half the district nurses questioned did not assess patients' pain. A recent clinical audit in Camden and Islington NHS Trust reported that 43 per cent of records demonstrated that pain was assessed but that the recording of the site (30 per cent) and nature (28 per cent) of the pain was relatively low (J Williams, *Summary Report of the Leg Ulcer Audit*, Camden and Islington Community Health Services NHS Trust, 1997).

31. In general, health authorities determine the level of provision of continence products for the population of patients that they serve. A survey commissioned by *Incontact* in 1997 found that most continence services had policies to determine the eligibility of patients to receive continence supplies through the NHS, as well as the quantity and type of supplies provided (B Anthony, *The Provision of Continence Supplies by NHS Trusts*, School of Health, Biological and Environmental Sciences, Middlesex University, 1997). It further reported that 12 per cent of continence services had a waiting list for the supply of continence pads and aids. Five of the study sites had criteria for the provision of continence products. These criteria stated who was eligible for products, when and what type of products would be issued. At one study site, a waiting list for new patients had been established. The average waiting time was three years.

32. The chart has two main purposes: as part of the baseline assessment of incontinence and as a record against which to evaluate progress. It is sometimes combined with measures of fluid intake to assess for its adequacy. An excessive intake, for example, may indicate metabolic disorders such as diabetes, while a low intake may result in constipation. A review of continence assessment forms in one study site in 1996 showed that only one in ten assessments included a frequency-volume chart.

33. It is difficult to prescribe an expected time to healing. The reasons why some venous leg ulcers fail to heal are poorly understood. However, the findings of this audit contrast with that at another study site where the leg ulcer service had a contract with the health authority that specified that 75 per cent of venous leg ulcers should be healed within 12 weeks, a proportion which is regularly exceeded.

34. In the Audit Commission's survey, one in six district nurses reported that they had never had specific training in the assessment of patients with leg ulcers, while more than one in five had no training in the assessment of incontinence.

35. Health authority returns for the fourth quarter of 1996/97 and 1997/98 show that more than 97 per cent of patients were visited within the two-hour timeband (source: unpublished data provided by the NHS Executive).

36. The UKCC highlights six key statements which are intended to assist the development and establishment of effective clinical supervision:

    • clinical supervision supports practice, enabling practitioners to maintain and promote standards of care;

    • clinical supervision is a practice-focused relationship where the practitioner reflects on practice and is guided by a skilled supervisor;

- the process of clinical supervision should be developed by practitioners and managers according to local circumstances. Ground rules should be agreed so that practitioners and supervisors approach clinical supervision openly, confidently and are aware of what is involved;

- every practitioner should have access to clinical supervision. Each supervisor should supervise a realistic number of practitioners;

- preparation for supervisors can be effected using in-house or external education programmes. The principles and relevance of clinical supervision should be included in pre- and post-registration education programmes; and

- evaluation of clinical supervision is needed to assess how it influences care, practice standards and the service. Evaluation systems should be determined locally.

37. Among community staff nurses, the proportion receiving clinical supervision was even lower at 38 per cent. Nurses working part-time, whether qualified district nurses or community staff nurses, were less likely to have taken part in clinical supervision and more likely to have done so on an infrequent basis.

38. There are a number of models of clinical supervision. One-to-one supervision is most common (47 per cent in the Commission's survey of nurses), followed by peer group support (27 per cent) and group supervision (24 per cent). In the study sites, it was more common to find a one-to-one model being used for G and H grades and a group model for other grades. In other cases, clinical supervision was currently available only to qualified district nurses.

39. One study site, audit revealed that of 21 supervisors in district nursing, only one was actively supervising and then supervising only one practitioner. In contrast, the same trust has 22 supervisors for health visiting who were supervising 58 individuals. At another trust, fewer than one-quarter of district nursing staff took part in the six half-day introductory workshops that were provided, and clinical supervisors have yet to be recruited. By contrast, 95 per cent of health visitors at this trust had attended clinical supervision workshops.

40. Other measures, less commonly quoted, include:
    - the prevalence of active ulceration;
    - the number of ulcer-free weeks in a defined period;
    - complication rates – adverse outcomes due, for example, to excessive compression or incorrectly treated arterial disease;
    - compliance with treatment;
    - patient satisfaction; and
    - clinic attendance rates.

    Different measures may be required for patients who are never going to achieve complete ulcer healing:
    - increased mobility;
    - reduced odour;
    - improved pain control;
    - less intrusive dressing regime;
    - increased independence;
    - increased socialisation;
    - proactive in own care;
    - improvements in self-image and self-esteem;
    - restoration of confidence;
    - awareness of continued professional support;
    - progression towards a healthy lifestyle; and
    - better understanding of their condition.

    Adapted from Community Healthcare Bolton NHS Trust, '*Community Leg Ulcer Service: Service Description*', November 1996.

41. Normally expressed as the proportion of leg ulcers that recur within a defined period (usually 12 or 24 months after healing).

42. The most important indicator of recurrence is patient compliance with compression hosiery. It is important that the patient understands that although the ulcer has healed, the underlying cause will remain (unless there is the possibility of surgical intervention). Compression is necessary to reduce the venous hypertension, otherwise the ulceration process is likely to begin again. Studies have shown a recurrence rate at 18 months of 20 per cent for patients with hosiery compared with 57 per cent in patients without. Some clinicians argue that the high recurrence rates reflect the fact that hospital referral is currently used as a last resort, and that thorough diagnostic and prognostic evaluation should be hospital-based and should include duplex scanning of the arterial and venous systems. This would enable early identification of patients who would benefit from treatment of vascular disease combined, if appropriate, with skin grafting (C V Ruckley, 'Caring for Patients with Chronic Leg Ulcer', *British Medical Journal*, Vol. 316, 1998, pp407-8).

43. In the Commission's survey, most district nurses at trusts where there is no clinical nurse specialist for tissue viability or continence reported getting information from colleagues, journals and pharmaceutical company reps.

44. The Audit Commission's survey of trusts found that, while the majority of trusts employed continence advisers, Macmillan nurses and diabetic nurse specialists, other specialist nurse posts were less common:

Continence	89%	Paediatric	40%
Macmillan	66%	Tissue viability	39%
Diabetic	53%	Stoma	35%

45. One of the differences between trusts is the extent to which clinical nurse specialists are involved with assessment and have their own caseload. In the case of tissue viability nurses, for example, there are three models:

    • the specialist does not hold a caseload but may accompany district nurses on assessment visits to provide expert advice and to observe practice;

    • in addition to providing advice, the specialist may carry a small caseload comprising particularly complex or difficult patients; and

    • the specialist undertakes all assessments (usually in a clinic setting) and provides all the clinical care until patients can be handed back to the generic district nursing service.

46. This study also found that clinics resulted in increased numbers of patients being treated because (a) the previously unmet needs of self-treating patients were identified and (b) increased referrals came from other healthcare professionals, including hospital consultants. While the increase in patients was substantial, it did not always result in an overall increase in face-to-face activity because:

    • increased healing rates reduced the number of face-to-face contacts within an episode of care; and

    • accurate assessment and more appropriate management reduced the number of dressing changes, thus reducing face-to-face contacts.

47. For example, in some trusts all leg ulcer link nurses are required to have completed the ENB N18 course, while continence link nurses will have completed the ENB 978 course.

48. The ratio of link nurses to district nurses varies considerably across study sites. For leg ulcer link nurses it ranged from 1:6 to 1:27, while for continence it ranged from 1:3 to 1:50.

49. Trusts record their expenditure on Trust Financial Return 2 (TFR2) against various expenditure codes. Code 108 of the form records 'Nursing' expenditure. The work unit for this code is district nursing contacts. However, trusts visited by the Audit Commission were inconsistent in the types of expenditure that they recorded against the code. In addition to district nursing, two of the trusts included health visiting and specialist nurses. One trust included school nursing and Macmillan nursing. Another trust included only district nurses, Macmillan nurses and Marie Curie nurses, while a fourth included district nursing expenditure only. These inconsistencies make TFR2 cost comparisons between trusts unreliable. The cost of district nursing services given here is based on the grade-mix of district nursing staff at 30 March 1997 as reported by trusts in the Audit Commission's national survey. Salary costs – top point for grades A, B, G, H and I and midpoint for grades D, E and F – are based on the recommended salary scales at 1 April 1998. In addition, there are employer's costs – estimated at 30 per cent – and other costs (for example, premises) – estimated at 22 per cent – of trust expenditure (based on the average distribution of expenditure at study sites). The quoted cost figure is adjusted for survey non-response.

50. Grade-mix has changed significantly in many district nursing services since publication of the NHS Management Executive's Value-For-Money Unit report on district nursing services (NHSME, *The Nursing Skill Mix in the District Nursing Service*, HMSO, 1992). The report, based on an activity sampling exercise in three community units, generated fierce controversy by concluding that G and H grade nurses were not utilising their skills as care managers to the full and were delivering care that could be delegated to community staff nurses. The study made radical recommendations, arguing that the service was top-heavy and that there could be cuts of up to 50 per cent in the numbers of G and H grade district nurses, enabling posts to be redistributed to 'care practitioners' and 'care assistants'. The approach used in the NHSME study was widely criticised. Nevertheless, in many trusts this is exactly the trajectory that staffing changes have followed, despite GP fundholders using their purchasing power to maintain grade-mix by insisting on having G grade district nursing sisters working with them.

51. That is, travel during working hours. Most of this travel is patient-related in that it is from one patient's home to another.

52. In 1992, the VFM Unit study (see note [50]) reported that qualified district nurses spent around 10 per cent of their time on patient management.

53. Administration was defined as paperwork not specific to any patient; meetings about the team, practice or trust business; telephone conversations with other staff (not about patients); and stock taking/ordering.

54. District nurses are not always able to follow up initial assessments because patients may have been referred at the weekend for a one-off visit – for example, a wound check – and are discharged before the district nurse can visit.

55.   At one trust, analysis of the top ten codes used by nursing auxiliaries to record their patient contact time shows that 86 per cent of activity was recorded as personal or social care.

56.   The community trust tried to counter this by paying all D grade bank nurses at the mid-point of the salary scale, rather than on the first incremental point. This will add 7 per cent to the forecast bank staff costs.

57.   In some trusts, the bank co-ordinator will cover all community nursing staff, not just district nursing.

58.   Bank staff may want to work only in certain locations. But because this information is seldom held centrally, bank co-ordinators waste time contacting nurses who are not available to work where the need has arisen.

59.   At the study site with a centralised bank and delegated budgets, bank nurses spent on average two-thirds of their time on patient care and patient management compared with half their time at the other trusts.

60.   In most trusts, visits at night are 'accompanied' or 'double-up' visits; that is, two members of staff visit the patient at the same time. This is mainly for the personal safety of the nurses.

61.   In one trust, district nursing teams were based within a number of health centres – each of the five teams taking it in turn to work at the weekend. In total, six nurses (one G grade, three staff nurses and two auxiliaries) divided into three teams, worked each weekend. The nurses provided care for patients registered with one of 35 GPs. Visits were delegated by the district nursing sister depending on the skills required. Wherever possible, visits were organised geographically. Some patients would attend the treatment room at the health centre where one of the registered nurses would be on duty.

62.   Two hundred and twenty-nine respondents were working in self-managed integrated teams and 148 in conventional district nursing teams.

63.   Nineteen per cent of district nurses working in integrated teams met formally with health visitors at least once a week, compared with 9 per cent in conventional teams; for meetings with practice nurses, the comparable figures were 22 per cent and 14 per cent; for GPs, 39 per cent and 30 per cent. Half the nurses in conventional teams said that they never met formally with social workers, compared with 30 per cent of those in integrated teams.

64.   A study of practices in Essex Rivers Health Care Trust (S Black and D Hagel, 'Developing an Integrated Nursing Team Approach', *Health Visitor*, Vol. 69, No. 7, 1996, pp280-3) found that integrated teams had completed practice health profiles, developed new services (for example, joint clinics for leg ulcers and immunisation), and developed joint protocols. Ear syringing and venepuncture were undertaken by district nurses and practice nurses while over-75 checks were carried out by all members of the nursing team. Joint packages of care were developed as a

contracting currency. The teams had also achieved greater flexibility of roles with the development of joint off-duty rotas and cover arrangements.

65.   For example: F Ross, E Rink, A Furne and M Gould, *Evolving Integrated Nursing Teams in Kingston Primary Care Services*, 1998 (unpublished report from the Joint Faculty of Healthcare Sciences, Kingston University and St George's Hospital Medical School and the Department of General Practice, St George's Hospital Medical School); J Smith, *99 George Street, Dumfries, Integrated Nursing Team Project: Evaluation Report*, Health Services Management Centre, University of Birmingham, 1998.

66.   One recent study (A Owen, 'Self-managed Teams: The West Berkshire Approach', *Health Visitor*, Vol. 71, No. 1, 1998, pp23-4) found no significant change in patient contact with the introduction of self-management. Training input to the teams was said to be high (at just under 3 per cent of the available time) during the initial stages of the pilot.

67.   In 1963 the Gillie Report recommended that district nurses and health visitors should be attached to particular GPs and their practice populations.
In 1974 the Gilmore Report identified the need to develop teamwork in primary care.
In 1981 the Harding Report highlighted the importance of multidisciplinary teams in primary healthcare and argued that such teams would function effectively only if team members had mutual respect for the role and skills of the others.
In 1986 the Cumberlege Report found that community nurses still functioned separately within set, inflexible roles and argued for a 'neighbourhood nursing service': integrated teams of district nurses, health visitors, school nurses, and their support staff, providing a service for, and responsive to, the needs of a defined geographical area.
In 1990 the Roy Report identified advantages of general practice-managed primary healthcare teams as offering an integrated approach to previously divided roles and responsibilities of practice nurses and health authority-employed nurses.
In 1993 *New World, New Opportunities* focused on the importance of teamworking.
In 1993 *A Vision for the Future* emphasised the need for partnerships between community nurses, other healthcare professionals, users and their carers.
The October 1996 White Paper, *Primary Care: Delivering the Future*, emphasised the role of primary healthcare teams in identifying health needs, planning, co-ordinating and delivering care.
The December 1996 White Paper, *Choice and Opportunity – Primary Care: The Future*, highlighted the team-based approach as essential to good quality primary care.

Index References are to paragraph numbers, Boxes, Case Studies and Case Histories

T

W